MathWise
Number Sense

With Answer Key

Peter Wise

MATH TEACHER,
MONUMENT,
COLORADO

CONTRIBUTOR

Katherine Wise

Cover Design by Kris Budi

Dedicated to my wife Allison

and my children David and Katherine

MathWise Number Sense with Answer Key

MathWise Curriculum Press

First printing 2016

MathWise Number Sense

TABLE OF CONTENTS

TABLE OF CONTENTS, CONTINUED

FOR WHICH GRADE LEVEL(S) ARE THESE BOOKS INTENDED?

This series is based on skill sets, not grade or age. These workbooks are intentionally created to be suitable for a wide range of grades. These books were part of the instruction in several different grade levels, and even in multi-grade math clubs. No one gets distracted by the grade level of the material. The concepts are the target.

MY EMPHASES IN TEACHING MATH

Too many students learn math as if they were learning a dead language. To them math consists of memorizing a bunch of rules and formulas. This is the wrong approach to learning math. To be good at math, it is important to know **how and why math works the way it does.** Students need to be trained to think mathematically from preschool through college, in every grade level. This formulaic understanding of math is both harder to learn and easier to forget.

Tips and tricks help as memory aids and have a legitimate role in acquiring and retaining information. However it is even more important that students understand the reasoning behind rules and formulas. **The MathWise series incorporates both tips/tricks as well as reasoning behind math formulas and procedures.**

TEACHING NUMBER SENSE

Number sense plays an important role in learning and understanding math. When students know their math facts and are able to manipulate numbers, it reduces their cognitive load, enabling them to concentrate more fully on the concepts. Mastering math facts also enables students to work at greater efficiency and speed so that they get more done in less time. This does not mean that students should be encouraged to rush through their math problems—it means that they don't spend excessive amounts of time doing simple calculations with numbers.

An additional benefit of increasing number sense is that students become better able to check their answers for reasonableness. This means that students will lose fewer points on quizzes and tests, because they develop a sharper eye for answers that can't be correct. They also develop a keener sense of the approximate value of the correct answer. In this respect, they are able to zoom in from the near answer to the exact answer.

Number sense also helps students to grow in their ability to see the big picture more clearly, without being bogged down with the numbers. If students are struggling with both numbers and concepts their cognitive load is doubled. Similarly language arts teachers know that if students are struggling with basic letters and phonics, it hinders their ability to comprehend the flow of a story.

The phrase, "drill and kill" is often held up as an argument against requiring students to memorize their basic math facts. Rote memorization of number basics is seen by some as a demand on children that erodes interest in math or stifles creativity.

My experience has shown me that the opposite is true. If a student takes twice as long to do a simple subtraction problem, then he or she is likely to take twice as long to complete a homework assignment. When a student has the additional cognitive load of the numbers, this added strain causes a undue lack of focus on the target concept.

Students who like math are usually those who don't struggle with numbers. They are able to easily calculate numbers as they proceed through math problems, often looking for clever ways to work smarter, not harder.

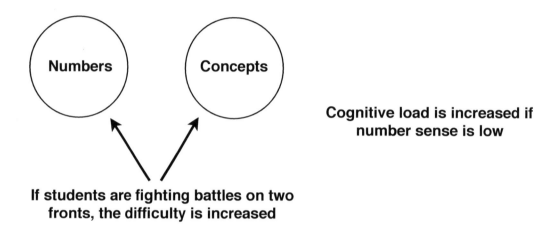

Numbers   **Concepts**

Cognitive load is increased if number sense is low

If students are fighting battles on two fronts, the difficulty is increased

Students who proceed to middle school or high school without proficiency with numbers will find that their difficulty with math will keep increasing and concepts will make less sense. Here is where the 'lack of drill' in earlier grades will really kill.

So instead of "drill and kill," I call it "drill and *skill.*" With a daily/weekly regimen in early grades of number drills and with the presentation of number sense concepts, students grow to enjoy numbers specifically and math in general.

Number sense should be taught in conjunction with every math concept presented. This is part of understanding how and why math works the way it does.

Discovering creative ways to solve problems is an additional benefit when students learn insights into number sense.

All of the *MathWise* books exemplify this emphasis on number sense. If students are working through the fractions or percents books, they are growing in their understanding of number sense in addition to learning about fractions or percents.

This book, however, is dedicated solely to number sense. It gives them insights and practice with essential skills, manipulation of numbers, and mental math. The foundation of number sense involves important skills such as doubling, halving, making tens, multiplying tens, rounding, estimating, and distributing. Along with this students should learn ways to manipulate numbers in order to optimize efficiency and check for reasonableness.

4 Quadrants of Math Instruction

Used in everyday life	*Efficiency of work* Speed Drills	*Depth of understanding* Slow, Careful Math	Used in school
Checks for reasonable-ness	*Utilization of number sense* Mental Math	*Technique* Show Lots of Work Math	Used for important financial matters

The above shows the four categories of math instruction that I use in my math instruction. On the left are Speed Drills and Mental Math. These are skill-builder categories that contribute to overall success in math. They are also more dependent on number sense than the categories on the right side.

In the first category, I give my students speed drills in class in order to promote math fact mastery. I do this daily at the beginning of the year, and less often as the year progresses. For me this is spending time to save time. The pace of my classes will increase as my students become faster at calculation. As the year progresses, more and more number crunching practice will occur in the context of solving textbook problems.

I also give my students mental math problems to solve. I call these "Math Blitz" problems. I read a series of addition, subtraction, multiplication, division problems and ask students to compute them mentally and write down just the answer. I don't use PEMDAS (order of operation) rules for this—just straight computation.

"Math Blitz" Card for Orally Given Mental Math Problems

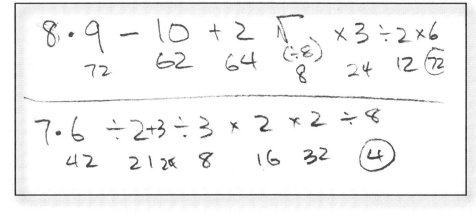

The quadrants on the left side are examples of math done in *everyday life*—especially when we are out in the real world.

The quadrants on the right side are examples on math done at school or with important financial matters. These are the ones that are really important, and the ones that I work the hardest to get students to be good at. These are also the ones that they most naturally resist!

Even though I have my students practice speed drills, I also require them to work at a sufficiently slow pace. "Finish first, finish worst!" is one of my frequent refrains. I refuse to accept tests or quizzes handed back too quickly. I do not allow my students to read a book or do anything else if they finish early. Students need to be able to change gears from speed drills to slow, careful math. Fast math helps slow math, but it is the slow math that really counts in life.

The last category, Show-Lots-of-Work Math, means that students need to develop habits of proper math technique rather than scribbling in random places.

MathWise books shine in the area of teaching good math technique. The answer boxes and sequenced problems make all the difference.

USING MATHWISE NUMBER SENSE

I find the *MathWise Number Sense* to be beneficial for students and accessible to almost every grade. The book starts out easy, but grows more challenging as the book goes on.

Students do not need to do every page, and teachers may pull sheets from different portions of the book to best meet the needs of the students.

It is my hope that this book will be a help to both teachers and students, and that the increase in skills will serve students well throughout their years in school and into their careers and lives.

Peter Wise
Monument, Colorado
2016

Web Site
For questions, comments, or suggestions, please visit
www.mathwisebooks.com.

Visual Math and Counting

Add the numbers on the dice

1. = ☐

2. = ☐

3. = ☐

4. = ☐

5. = ☐

6. = ☐

Skip count forwards and backwards

7. Skip count by 2s

   <u> 1 </u>   <u> 3 </u>   <u>   </u>   <u> 7 </u>   <u>   </u>   <u> 11 </u>   <u>   </u>   <u> 15 </u>   <u>   </u>   <u> 19 </u>   <u>   </u>   <u>   </u>

8. Skip count by 2s

   <u> 2 </u>   <u>   </u>   <u>   </u>   <u>   </u>   <u>   </u>   <u>   </u>   <u>   </u>   <u>   </u>   <u>   </u>   <u>   </u>

9. Skip count backwards by 2s

   <u> 30 </u>   <u>   </u>   <u>   </u>   <u>   </u>   <u>   </u>   <u>   </u>   <u>   </u>   <u>   </u>   <u>   </u>   <u>   </u>

Add the following coins

10. (10¢) (25¢) (5¢)

    = ☐ ¢

11. (50¢) (25¢) (1¢) (1¢)

    = ☐ ¢

1

Visual Math and Counting

Add the numbers on the dice

1. :::: :::: = ☐   **4.** :: :: :::: = ☐

2. :: :: = ☐   **5.** :: :: :: = ☐

3. :: :: = ☐   **6.** :: :::: :: = ☐

Skip count forwards and backwards

7. Skip count by 2s

32 ___ 36 ___ ___ ___ 44 ___ ___ ___ ___ 54

8. Skip count by 3s

3 ___ ___ 12 ___ ___ ___ 24 ___ ___ 33 ___

9. Skip count by 10s

17 ___ ___ ___ 57 ___ ___ ___ 97 ___ ___ ___

Add the following coins

10. (25¢) (25¢) (25¢) (10¢) (5¢)   **11.** (25¢) (10¢) (5¢) (5¢)

= ☐ ¢   = ☐ ¢

Visual Math and Counting

Add the numbers on the dice

1.  =

4.   =

2.   =

5.   =

3.   =

6.   =

Skip count forwards and backwards

7. Skip count backwards by 2s

    24 ___ ___ ___ 16 ___ ___ ___ ___ ___ ___

8. Skip count forwards by 5s

    75 ___ ___ ___ ___ ___ ___ 110 ___ ___ ___

9. Skip count forwards by 10s

    260 ___ ___ ___ ___ ___ ___ ___ ___ ___ ___

Add the following coins

10.

    = ¢

Visual Math and Counting

Add the following dice

1. 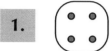 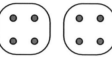 = ☐   4.   =

2.   = ☐   5.   = ☐

3.   =   6.   = ☐

Skip count forwards and backwards

7. Skip backwards by 2s

   112 ___ ___ ___ ___ ___ ___ ___ ___ ___

8. Skip count forwards by 25s (like counting by quarters with money)

   25 ___ ___ 100 ___ ___ ___ ___ ___

9. Skip count backwards by 10s

   113 ___ ___ ___ ___ ___ ___ ___ ___

Add the following coins

10. (25¢) (10¢) (10¢) (10¢) (10¢) (5¢) (5¢) (5¢) (5¢)

    35¢ ___ 55¢ ___ ___ ___ ___ ☐ ¢

4

Making Tens

$0 + \boxed{} = 10$

$1 + \boxed{} = 10$

$2 + \boxed{} = 10$

$3 + \boxed{} = 10$

$4 + \boxed{} = 10$

$5 + 5 = 10$

$6 + \boxed{} = 10$

$7 + \boxed{} = 10$

$8 + \boxed{} = 10$

$9 + \boxed{} = 10$

$10 + \boxed{} = 10$

Sets are the reverse of each other!

1. $3 + \boxed{} = 10$

2. $6 + \boxed{} = 10$

3. $2 + \boxed{} = 10$

4. $1 + \boxed{} = 10$

5. $4 + \boxed{} = 10$

6. $7 + \boxed{} = 10$

7. $8 + \boxed{} = 10$

8. $5 + \boxed{} = 10$

9. $7 + \boxed{} = 10$

10. $6 + \boxed{} = 10$

11. $9 + \boxed{} = 10$

12. $8 + \boxed{} = 10$

SAME IDEA, BUT WITH 3 NUMBERS!

13. $3 + 2 + \boxed{} = 10$

14. $5 + 3 + \boxed{} = 10$

15. $2 + 5 + \boxed{} = 10$

16. $3 + 3 + \boxed{} = 10$

SIMILAR IDEA—BUT MAKE 20S!

17. $18 + \boxed{} = 20$

18. $14 + \boxed{} = 20$

19. $15 + \boxed{} = 20$

20. $17 + \boxed{} = 20$

21. $12 + \boxed{} = 20$

22. $13 + \boxed{} = 20$

23. $16 + \boxed{} = 20$

24. $11 + \boxed{} = 20$

5

Adding by Looking for Tens

A. ③
4
+ ⑦
_____

#1 LOOK FOR NUMBERS THAT ADD UP TO 10!

ADD THOSE FIRST!

⑩ + 4 = 14

#2 ADD THE NUMBERS THAT ARE LEFT OVER!

B. 8
3
+ 2
_____

WHEN YOU DO THESE PROBLEMS, YOU MAY FIND IT EASIER TO DRAW CONNECTING LINES TO THE NUMBERS THAT ADD UP TO 10!

⑩ + 3 = 13

Draw connector lines to the numbers that make 10; add the extra number(s) to get your final answer

IN THIS LAST COLUMN LOOK FOR THREE NUMBERS THAT ADD UP TO 10!

---

1. 4
6
+ 9
_____

4. 5
4
3
+ 5
_____

7. 5
3
5
+ 7
_____

10. 5
3
2
+ 1
_____

2. 1
8
+ 9
_____

5. 3
6
5
+ 4
_____

8. 2
1
4
+ 9
_____

11. 3
3
2
+ 4
_____

3. 5
7
+ 3
_____

6. 8
1
3
+ 2
_____

9. 4
7
3
+ 6
_____

12. 3
6
8
+ 1
_____

Making Tens with Three Numbers

Example

A. $3 + 1 + \boxed{6} = 10$

Make tens by finding the missing numbers

1. $2 + 7 + \boxed{} = 10$

2. $5 + 2 + \boxed{} = 10$

3. $2 + 4 + \boxed{} = 10$

4. $3 + 5 + \boxed{} = 10$

5. $1 + 3 + \boxed{} = 10$

6. $4 + 2 + \boxed{} = 10$

7. $2 + 5 + \boxed{} = 10$

8. $2 + 2 + \boxed{} = 10$

9. $6 + 2 + \boxed{} = 10$

10. $2 + 5 + \boxed{} = 10$

Make tens by finding the missing numbers (now with subtraction)

11. $3 - 1 + \boxed{} = 10$

12. $8 - 2 + \boxed{} = 10$

13. $8 - 3 + \boxed{} = 10$

14. $5 - 2 + \boxed{} = 10$

15. $8 - 5 + \boxed{} = 10$

16. $3 - 1 + \boxed{} = 10$

17. $9 - 2 + \boxed{} = 10$

18. $9 - 5 + \boxed{} = 10$

7

Making Thirty and Fifty

A. THINK OF THIS PROBLEM AS: 10 + 10 + (2 + 8)!

(20) → 12 ←
       → 18 ← (10)

$$\begin{array}{r} 20 \\ 10 \\ \hline 30 \end{array}$$

B. THINK OF THIS PROBLEM AS: 20 + 20 + (1 + 9)!

(40) → 29 ←
       → 21 ← (10)

$$\begin{array}{r} 40 \\ 10 \\ \hline 50 \end{array}$$

Make 30s by adding tens on the left and right columns	Make 50s by adding tens on the left and right columns

1.
$$\begin{array}{r} 1\ 3 \\ +\ 1\ \square \\ \hline 3\ 0 \end{array}$$

6.
$$\begin{array}{r} 1\ 2 \\ +\ \square \\ \hline 3\ 0 \end{array}$$

11.
$$\begin{array}{r} 2\ 3 \\ +\ 2\ \square \\ \hline 5\ 0 \end{array}$$

16.
$$\begin{array}{r} 2\ 8 \\ +\ \square \\ \hline 5\ 0 \end{array}$$

2.
$$\begin{array}{r} 1\ 6 \\ +\ 1\ \square \\ \hline 3\ 0 \end{array}$$

7.
$$\begin{array}{r} 1\ 9 \\ +\ \square \\ \hline 3\ 0 \end{array}$$

12.
$$\begin{array}{r} 2\ 5 \\ +\ 2\ \square \\ \hline 5\ 0 \end{array}$$

17.
$$\begin{array}{r} 3\ 7 \\ +\ \square \\ \hline 5\ 0 \end{array}$$

3.
$$\begin{array}{r} 1\ 5 \\ +\ 1\ \square \\ \hline 3\ 0 \end{array}$$

8.
$$\begin{array}{r} 1\ 4 \\ +\ \square \\ \hline 3\ 0 \end{array}$$

13.
$$\begin{array}{r} 2\ 6 \\ +\ 2\ \square \\ \hline 5\ 0 \end{array}$$

18.
$$\begin{array}{r} 3\ 2 \\ +\ \square \\ \hline 5\ 0 \end{array}$$

4.
$$\begin{array}{r} 1\ 8 \\ +\ 1\ \square \\ \hline 3\ 0 \end{array}$$

9.
$$\begin{array}{r} 1\ 3 \\ +\ \square \\ \hline 3\ 0 \end{array}$$

14.
$$\begin{array}{r} 2\ 1 \\ +\ 2\ \square \\ \hline 5\ 0 \end{array}$$

19.
$$\begin{array}{r} 3\ 6 \\ +\ \square \\ \hline 5\ 0 \end{array}$$

5.
$$\begin{array}{r} 1\ 1 \\ +\ 1\ \square \\ \hline 3\ 0 \end{array}$$

10.
$$\begin{array}{r} 1\ 8 \\ +\ \square \\ \hline 3\ 0 \end{array}$$

15.
$$\begin{array}{r} 2\ 2 \\ +\ 2\ \square \\ \hline 5\ 0 \end{array}$$

20.
$$\begin{array}{r} 3\ 1 \\ +\ \square \\ \hline 5\ 0 \end{array}$$

Adding Tens and Ones

Examples

A.	3 tens and 8	B.	14 tens and 8	C.	15 tens and 18
	3 tens = 30 + 8 = $\boxed{38}$		14 tens = 140 + 8 = $\boxed{148}$		15 tens = 150 + 18 = $\boxed{168}$

Calculate the tens and the ones; then add them together

1. 4 tens and 3 =

2. 4 tens and 13 =

> THERE IS ONE MORE TEN HERE!

3. 15 tens =

4. 15 tens and 2 =

5. 15 tens and 12 =

6. 6 tens and 14 =

7. 3 tens and 10 =

8. 3 tens and 11 =

9. 8 tens and 20 =

10. 12 tens and 25 =

> TWO MORE TENS HERE!

11. 17 tens and 14 =

12. 16 tens and 30 =

13. 16 tens and 38 =

14. 7 tens and 5 =

15. 7 tens and 15 =

16. 6 tens and 40 =

17. 6 tens and 45 =

18. 19 tens and 10 =

19. 19 tens and 17 =

20. 19 tens and 37 =

21. 8 tens and 30 =

22. 8 tens and 42 =

23. 7 tens and 30 =

24. 7 tens and 34 =

9

Adding Tens and Ones

1. 5 tens and 7 = _____

2. 5 tens and 17 = _____

3. 6 tens and 25 = _____

4. 14 tens and 7 = _____

5. 14 tens and 37 = _____

6. 8 tens and 20 = _____

7. 8 tens and 28 = _____

8. 7 tens and 46 = _____

9. 16 tens and 4 = _____

10. 16 tens and 24 = _____

11. 25 tens and 7 = _____

12. 25 tens and 17 = _____

13. 12 tens and 45 = _____

14. 7 tens and 53 = _____

15. 6 tens and 38 = _____

16. 18 tens and 54 = _____

FIND THE MISSING NUMBER! (MAKING 10S!)

17. 8 + _____ = 10

18. 13 + _____ = 20

19. 26 + _____ = 30

20. 4 + _____ = 10

21. 11 + _____ = 20

22. 23 + _____ = 30

23. 16 + _____ = 20

24. 12 + _____ = 20

25. 25 + _____ = 30

FIND THE MISSING NUMBERS IN THE SERIES!

26. 13 23 33 _____ _____ 63

27. 47 57 _____ _____ 87

28. 97 87 77 _____ _____ 47

29. 122 112 _____ _____ _____

© Peter Wise, 2016

10

Adding Tens and Ones

1. 6 tens and 2 = ☐

2. 6 tens and 12 = ☐

3. 6 tens and 22 = ☐

4. 16 tens and 2 = ☐

5. 16 tens and 42 = ☐

6. 5 tens and 37 = ☐

7. 9 tens and 15 = ☐

8. 7 tens and 39 = ☐

9. 2 tens and 37 = ☐

10. 3 tens and 71 = ☐

11. 11 tens and 8 = ☐

12. 11 tens and 28 = ☐

13. 1 ten and 14 = ☐

14. 7 tens and 57 = ☐

15. 8 tens and 35 = ☐

16. 18 tens and 35 = ☐

FIND THE MISSING NUMBER! (MAKING 10S!)

17. 12 + ☐ = 20

18. 13 + ☐ = 20

19. 3 + ☐ = 20

20. 14 + ☐ = 20

21. 4 + ☐ = 20

22. 9 + ☐ = 20

23. 2 + ☐ = 20

24. 18 + ☐ = 20

25. 13 + ☐ = 20

FIND THE MISSING NUMBERS IN THE SERIES!

26. 72 82 92 ☐ ☐ 122

27. 65 55 ☐ ☐ 25

28. 79 69 59 ☐ ☐ ☐

29. 117 107 ☐ ☐ ☐

Adding Tens and Ones

1. 9 tens and 8 = ☐

2. 9 tens and 18 = ☐

3. 9 tens and 23 = ☐

4. 9 tens and 93 = ☐

5. 4 tens and 42 = ☐

6. 3 tens and 61 = ☐

7. 13 tens and 27 = ☐

8. 8 tens and 51 = ☐

9. 19 tens and 7 = ☐

10. 19 tens and 27 = ☐

11. 28 tens and 4 = ☐

12. 28 tens and 24 = ☐

13. 4 tens and 125 = ☐

14. 5 tens and 139 = ☐

15. 12 tens and 45 = ☐

16. 8 tens and 71 = ☐

FIND THE MISSING NUMBER! (MAKING 10S!)

17. 7 + ☐ = 30

18. 12 + ☐ = 30

19. 6 + ☐ = 30

20. 3 + ☐ = 50

21. 41 + ☐ = 50

22. 31 + ☐ = 50

23. 94 + ☐ = 100

24. 84 + ☐ = 100

25. 89 + ☐ = 100

FIND THE MISSING NUMBERS IN THE SERIES!

26. 14 24 34 ☐ ☐ 64

27. 88 98 ☐ ☐ 128

28. 92 82 72 ☐ ☐ 42

29. 133 123 ☐ ☐ ☐

Mixed Review

Draw connector lines to the numbers that make 10, then add

1.
5
7
2
+ 5
☐

2.
2
4
3
+ 6
☐

3.
8
1
2
+ 6
☐

4.
3
9
5
+ 1
☐

Make tens by finding the missing numbers

5. $5 + 3 + \boxed{} = 10$

7. $2 + 3 + \boxed{} = 10$

6. $3 + 4 + \boxed{} = 10$

8. $2 + 4 + \boxed{} = 10$

Make 30s by finding the missing numbers

9.
1 2
+ 1 ☐
―――
3 0

10.
1 6
+ 1 ☐
―――
3 0

11.
1 3
+ ☐
―――
3 0

12.
1 1
+ ☐
―――
3 0

Calculate the tens and the ones; then add them together

13. 3 tens and 2 = ☐

16. 12 tens and 14 = ☐

14. 3 tens and 12 = ☐

17. 9 tens and 56 = ☐

15. 6 tens and 15 = ☐

18. 8 tens and 25 = ☐

13

Making Tens and More

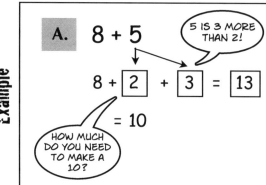

A. 8 + 5

5 IS 3 MORE THAN 2!

8 + ☐2☐ + ☐3☐ = ☐13☐

= 10

HOW MUCH DO YOU NEED TO MAKE A 10?

Break up numbers to make 10s (or multiples of 10)!

Sometimes referred to as Number Decomposition

You are really rearranging numbers to make 10s

Example

Add numbers by making 10s

1. 7 + 5

7 + ☐ + ☐ = ☐

= 10

2. 5 + 9

5 + ☐ + ☐ = ☐

= 10

3. 3 + 8

3 + ☐ + ☐ = ☐

= 10

4. 8 + 6

8 + ☐ + ☐ = ☐

= 10

5. 2 + 9

2 + ☐ + ☐ = ☐

= 10

6. 7 + 9

7 + ☐ + ☐ = ☐

= 10

7. 8 + 15

4 + ☐ + ☐ = ☐

= 10

8. 6 + 28

4 + ☐ + ☐ = ☐

= 10

How Much More Than 10?

Example

A. 7 + 5

7 + [3] + [2] = [12]
= 10

Add the following numbers by making 10s

1. 8 + 3

8 + [ ] + [ ] = [ ]
= 10

6. 4 + 8

4 + [ ] + [ ] = [ ]
= 10

2. 9 + 4

9 + [ ] + [ ] = [ ]
= 10

7. 6 + 7

6 + [ ] + [ ] = [ ]
= 10

3. 8 + 6

8 + [ ] + [ ] = [ ]
= 10

8. 9 + 6

9 + [ ] + [ ] = [ ]
= 10

4. 5 + 8

5 + [ ] + [ ] = [ ]
= 10

9. 8 + 9

8 + [ ] + [ ] = [ ]
= 10

5. 7 + 8

7 + [ ] + [ ] = [ ]
= 10

10. 4 + 7

4 + [ ] + [ ] = [ ]
= 10

15

How Much More Than 20?

Example

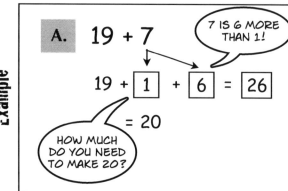

A. 19 + 7

7 IS 6 MORE THAN 1!

19 + ☐1☐ + ☐6☐ = ☐26☐

HOW MUCH DO YOU NEED TO MAKE 20?

= 20

Break up numbers to make 20s (just like you did with 10s)

20 is the just the second ten

You are really rearranging numbers to make 20 plus some amount

---

Add the following numbers by making 20s

1. 16 + 5

16 + ☐ + ☐ = ☐

= 20   answer

2. 19 + 8

19 + ☐ + ☐ = ☐

= 20

3. 14 + 8

14 + ☐ + ☐ = ☐

= 20

4. 17 + 9

17 + ☐ + ☐ = ☐

= 20

5. 13 + 9

13 + ☐ + ☐ = ☐

= 20

6. 18 + 7

18 + ☐ + ☐ = ☐

= 20

7. 17 + 6

17 + ☐ + ☐ = ☐

= 20

8. 15 + 7

15 + ☐ + ☐ = ☐

= 20

How Much More Than 20?

Example

A. 15 + 6

15 + [5] + [1] = [21]

= 20   answer

Add the following numbers by making 20s

1. 18 + 5

18 + [ ] + [ ] = [   ]

= 20   answer

2. 17 + 9

17 + [ ] + [ ] = [   ]

= 20

3. 15 + 7

15 + [ ] + [ ] = [   ]

= 20

4. 14 + 9

14 + [ ] + [ ] = [   ]

= 20

5. 19 + 7

19 + [ ] + [ ] = [   ]

= 20

6. 13 + 8

13 + [ ] + [ ] = [   ]

= 20

7. 18 + 9

18 + [ ] + [ ] = [   ]

= 20

8. 17 + 8

17 + [ ] + [ ] = [   ]

= 20

© Peter Wise, 2016

17

Adding Neighbors (Close Numbers)

Add the following close numbers

1. $7 + 7 =$ ▢

$7 + 8 =$ ▢

2. $6 + 6 =$ ▢

$6 + 7 =$ ▢

3. $8 + 8 =$ ▢

$8 + 9 =$ ▢

4. $3 + 3 =$ ▢

$3 + 4 =$ ▢

5. $5 + 5 =$ ▢

$5 + 6 =$ ▢

6. $9 + 9 =$ ▢

$9 + 8 =$ ▢

7. $12 + 12 =$ ▢

$12 + 13 =$ ▢

8. $11 + 11 =$ ▢

$11 + 12 =$ ▢

9. $15 + 15 =$ ▢

$15 + 16 =$ ▢

10. $14 + 14 =$ ▢

$14 + 15 =$ ▢

Skip count

11. By 20s: __20__ __40__ ___ ___ ___ ___ ___ ___

12. By 30s: __30__ __60__ ___ ___ ___ ___ ___ ___

One More 10 for the Fives

Example

A.

both fives add up to 10

$[10]$

$35 + 35 = 70$

$[60]$ $30 + 30 = 60$ Now add the numbers in the boxes: $60 + 10 = 70$

Adding two fives gives you one more ten

Find the sums of the following numbers

1. $15 + 15 = [\ \ ]$

   [ ] ADD THE 5'S

   [ ] ADD THE 10'S

   ADD THE AMOUNTS IN THE TWO BOXES!

2. [ ] add the 5s

   $25 + 25 = [\ \ ]$

   [ ] add the tens place

3. [ ] add the 5s

   $45 + 45 = [\ \ ]$

   [ ] add the tens place

4. [ ] add the 5s

   $75 + 75 = [\ \ ]$

   [ ] add the tens place

5. [ ] ones place

   $55 + 55 = [\ \ ]$

   [ ] tens place

6. [ ] fives

   $95 + 95 = [\ \ ]$

   [ ] tens place

7. [ ] fives

   $65 + 65 = [\ \ ]$

   [ ] tens place

8. [ ] fives

   $45 + 35 = [\ \ ]$

   [ ] tens place

9. [ ] fives

   $35 + 75 = [\ \ ]$

   [ ] add the tens place

Add More Tens

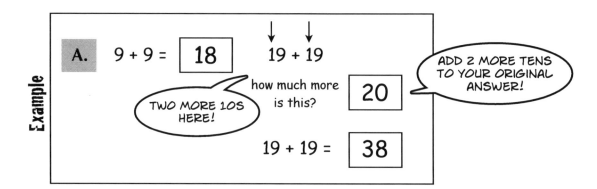

A. 9 + 9 = [18]   ↓ ↓ 19 + 19

how much more is this? [20]

TWO MORE 10S HERE!

ADD 2 MORE TENS TO YOUR ORIGINAL ANSWER!

19 + 19 = [38]

Add the original numbers, add the additional tens, solve the new problems

1. 7 + 2 = [   ]   17 + 12

how much more is this? [   ]

17 + 12 = [   ]

5. 12 + 4 = [   ]   22 + 14

how much more is this? [   ]

22 + 14 = [   ]

2. 3 + 5 = [   ]   13 + 15

how much more is this? [   ]

13 + 15 = [   ]

6. 17 + 7 = [   ]   37 + 27

how much more is this? [   ]

37 + 27 = [   ]

3. 6 + 9 = [   ]   26 + 19

how much more is this? [   ]

26 + 19 = [   ]

7. 15 + 6 = [   ]   35 + 16

how much more is this? [   ]

35 + 16 = [   ]

4. 5 + 8 = [   ]   25 + 28

how much more is this? [   ]

25 + 28 = [   ]

8. 14 + 5 = [   ]   44 + 15

how much more is this? [   ]

44 + 15 = [   ]

Add More Tens

Add the original numbers, add the additional tens, solve the new problems

1. 5 + 6 = [ ]   15 + 16
how much more is this? [ ]

15 + 16 = [ ]

2. 8 + 8 = [ ]   18 + 28
how much more is this? [ ]

18 + 28 = [ ]

3. 7 + 7 = [ ]   27 + 27
how much more is this? [ ]

27 + 27 = [ ]

4. 13 + 6 = [ ]   23 + 26
how much more is this? [ ]

23 + 26 = [ ]

5. 9 + 9 = [ ]   39 + 39
how much more is this? [ ]

39 + 39 = [ ]

6. 14 + 5 = [ ]   34 + 25
how much more is this? [ ]

34 + 25 = [ ]

7. 6 + 7 = [ ]   26 + 7
how much more is this? [ ]

26 + 7 = [ ]

8. 19 + 7 = [ ]   29 + 27
how much more is this? [ ]

29 + 27 = [ ]

9. 15 + 9 = [ ]   25 + 39
how much more is this? [ ]

25 + 39 = [ ]

10. 18 + 7 = [ ]   48 + 27
how much more is this? [ ]

48 + 27 = [ ]

21

Adding as Doubles +1 or -1

Example

A. 4 + 5 =   ⬚4 + ⬚4 + 1 = 9   Double the lower number + 1

5 IS JUST ONE MORE THAN 4!

⬚5 + ⬚5 – 1 = 9   Double the higher number - 1

Add the following close numbers

1. 5 + 6 =

☐ + ☐ + 1 = ☐   Double the lower number

☐ + ☐ – 1 = ☐   Double the higher number

2. 6 + 7 =

☐ + ☐ + 1 = ☐

3. 8 + 9 =

☐ + ☐ – 1 = ☐

4. 7 + 8 =

☐ + ☐ – 1 = ☐

5. 10 + 11 =

☐ + ☐ + 1 = ☐

6. 15 + 16 =

☐ + ☐ + 1 = ☐

Skip count

11. By 8s: __8__ ___ ___ ___ ___ ___ ___ ___

8 IS "UP A 10, DOWN A 2"!

12. By 12s: __12__ ___ ___ ___ ___ ___ ___ ___

12 IS "UP A 10, UP A 2"!

22

Adding Twins and Close Numbers

1. 4 + 4 = ☐
   4 + 5 = ☐
   ☐ more

2. 3 + 3 = ☐
   3 + 5 = ☐
   ☐ more

3. 7 + 7 = ☐
   7 + 8 = ☐
   ☐ more

4. 6 + 6 = ☐
   6 + 8 = ☐
   ☐ more

5. 8 + 8 = ☐
   8 + 9 = ☐
   ☐ more

6. 5 + 5 = ☐
   5 + 7 = ☐
   ☐ more

7. 7 + 7 = ☐
   7 + 9 = ☐
   ☐ more

8. 6 + 6 = ☐
   6 + 7 = ☐
   ☐ more

9. 5 + 5 = ☐
   5 + 8 = ☐
   ☐ more

10. 9 + 9 = ☐
    9 + 11 = ☐
    ☐ more

23

Doubling Numbers

1. $\begin{array}{r} +\ 7 \\ 7 \\ \hline \end{array}$

2. $\begin{array}{r} +\ 9 \\ 9 \\ \hline \end{array}$

3. $\begin{array}{r} +\ 8 \\ 8 \\ \hline \end{array}$

4. $\begin{array}{r} +\ 6 \\ 6 \\ \hline \end{array}$

5. $\begin{array}{r} +\ 17 \\ 17 \\ \hline \end{array}$

6. $\begin{array}{r} +\ 19 \\ 19 \\ \hline \end{array}$

7. $\begin{array}{r} +\ 14 \\ 14 \\ \hline \end{array}$

8. $\begin{array}{r} +\ 15 \\ 15 \\ \hline \end{array}$

9. $\begin{array}{r} +\ 28 \\ 28 \\ \hline \end{array}$

10. $\begin{array}{r} +\ 24 \\ 24 \\ \hline \end{array}$

11. $\begin{array}{r} +\ 26 \\ 26 \\ \hline \end{array}$

12. $\begin{array}{r} +\ 39 \\ 39 \\ \hline \end{array}$

13. $\begin{array}{r} +\ 34 \\ 34 \\ \hline \end{array}$

14. $\begin{array}{r} +\ 27 \\ 27 \\ \hline \end{array}$

15. $\begin{array}{r} +\ 18 \\ 18 \\ \hline \end{array}$

16. $\begin{array}{r} +\ 36 \\ 36 \\ \hline \end{array}$

17. $\begin{array}{r} +\ 45 \\ 45 \\ \hline \end{array}$

18. $\begin{array}{r} +\ 38 \\ 38 \\ \hline \end{array}$

19. $\begin{array}{r} +\ 29 \\ 29 \\ \hline \end{array}$

20. $\begin{array}{r} +\ 47 \\ 47 \\ \hline \end{array}$

Doubling Numbers

1. $\begin{array}{r} 16 \\ + 16 \\ \hline \end{array}$

2. $\begin{array}{r} 19 \\ + 19 \\ \hline \end{array}$

3. $\begin{array}{r} 14 \\ + 14 \\ \hline \end{array}$

4. $\begin{array}{r} 18 \\ + 18 \\ \hline \end{array}$

5. $\begin{array}{r} 17 \\ + 17 \\ \hline \end{array}$

6. $\begin{array}{r} 15 \\ + 15 \\ \hline \end{array}$

7. $\begin{array}{r} 23 \\ + 23 \\ \hline \end{array}$

8. $\begin{array}{r} 27 \\ + 27 \\ \hline \end{array}$

9. $\begin{array}{r} 26 \\ + 26 \\ \hline \end{array}$

10. $\begin{array}{r} 29 \\ + 29 \\ \hline \end{array}$

11. $\begin{array}{r} 28 \\ + 28 \\ \hline \end{array}$

12. $\begin{array}{r} 32 \\ + 32 \\ \hline \end{array}$

13. $\begin{array}{r} 37 \\ + 37 \\ \hline \end{array}$

14. $\begin{array}{r} 36 \\ + 36 \\ \hline \end{array}$

15. $\begin{array}{r} 34 \\ + 34 \\ \hline \end{array}$

16. $\begin{array}{r} 35 \\ + 35 \\ \hline \end{array}$

17. $\begin{array}{r} 49 \\ + 49 \\ \hline \end{array}$

18. $\begin{array}{r} 45 \\ + 45 \\ \hline \end{array}$

19. $\begin{array}{r} 47 \\ + 47 \\ \hline \end{array}$

20. $\begin{array}{r} 48 \\ + 48 \\ \hline \end{array}$

Doubling Numbers

Double the following numbers

**5 or more in the ONES place will give you a CARRY
if you carry, add one more to the TENS place**

1. 12 → ☐

2. 14 → ☐

3. 15 → ☐

4. 17 → ☐

5. 13 → ☐

6. 19 → ☐

7. 18 → ☐

8. 26 → ☐

9. 23 → ☐

10. 27 → ☐

11. 22 → ☐

12. 29 → ☐

13. 31 → ☐   when 5 more
is doubled,
it becomes
10 more

5 more ↓   ↓

14. 36 → ☐

15. 34 → ☐

16. 35 → ☐

17. 16 → ☐

18. 42 → ☐

19. 47 → ☐

20. 43 → ☐

21. 38 → ☐

22. 46 → ☐

23. 37 → ☐

24. 49 → ☐

Doubling Numbers

Add the following twin numbers				

1. $6 + 6 =$ ☐   **11.** $23 + 23 =$ ☐

2. $8 + 8 =$ ☐   **12.** $34 + 34 =$ ☐

3. $4 + 4 =$ ☐   **13.** $17 + 17 =$ ☐

4. $7 + 7 =$ ☐   **14.** $41 + 41 =$ ☐

5. $9 + 9 =$ ☐   **15.** $70 + 70 =$ ☐

6. $12 + 12 =$ ☐   **16.** $74 + 74 =$ ☐

7. $11 + 11 =$ ☐   **17.** $26 + 26 =$ ☐

8. $15 + 15 =$ ☐   **18.** $38 + 38 =$ ☐

9. $13 + 13 =$ ☐   **19.** $24 + 24 =$ ☐

10. $14 + 14 =$ ☐   **20.** $108 + 108 =$ ☐

Review Problems

21. $14 +$ ☐ $= 20$ **24.** 4 tens and 7 $=$ ☐

22. $17 +$ ☐ $= 20$ **25.** 4 tens and 17 $=$ ☐

23. $12 +$ ☐ $= 20$ **26.** 7 tens and 25 $=$ ☐

27

Doubling Numbers Left to Right

Example

If the is place number is 5 or more add one to the tens place

$$18 + 18 = 3\ 6$$

#1   Check if the 1s place digit is 5 or more

#2   Add the TENS place FIRST, but add one if the tens place number is 5 or more

#3   Double the ONES place number, but just write the last digit (1s place)

1 + 1 = 2, but you need to add one more because of the carry.

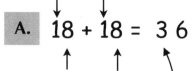

A. $18 + 18 = 3\ 6$

5 or more in the 1s place will give you a CARRY. The 10s place will go UP ONE

Double the following numbers by going LEFT to RIGHT

1.   17 + 17 =

will you have a carry?   y   n

add the TENS place
add 1 more if a carry → ☐ ☐

add the ONES place
LAST digit only

2.   13 + 13 =

will you have a carry?   y   n

add the TENS place
add 1 more if a carry → ☐ ☐

add the ONES place
LAST digit only

3.   19 + 19 =

will you have a carry?   y   n

add the TENS place
add 1 more if a carry → ☐ ☐

add the ONES place
LAST digit only

4.   26 + 26 =

will you have a carry?   y   n

add the TENS place
add 1 more if a carry → ☐ ☐

add the ONES place
LAST digit only

5.   48 + 48 =

will you have a carry?   y   n

add the TENS place
add 1 more if a carry → ☐ ☐

add the ONES place

6.   45 + 45 =

will you have a carry?   y   n

add the TENS place
add 1 more if a carry → ☐ ☐

add the ONES place

28

Doubling Numbers Left to Right

1. 18 + 18 =

add the TENS place
add 1 more if a carry → ☐☐

add the ONES place
LAST digit only

2. 35 + 35 =

add the TENS place
add 1 more if a carry → ☐☐

add the ONES place
LAST digit only

3. 24 + 24 =

add the TENS place
add 1 more if a carry → ☐☐

add the ONES place

4. 43 + 43 =

add the TENS place
add 1 more if a carry → ☐☐

add the ONES place

5. 29 + 29 =

add the TENS place
add 1 more if a carry → ☐☐

add the ONES place

6. 32 + 32 =

add the TENS place
add 1 more if a carry → ☐☐

add the ONES place
LAST digit only

7. 27 + 27 =

add the TENS place
add 1 more if a carry → ☐☐

add the ONES place

8. 49 + 49 =

add the TENS place
add 1 more if a carry → ☐☐

add the ONES place

9. 36 + 36 =

add the TENS place
add 1 more if a carry → ☐☐

add the ONES place

10. 46 + 46 =

add the TENS place
add 1 more if a carry → ☐☐

add the ONES place

Doubling Numbers Left to Right

Example

1 + 1 = 2, but you need to add one more because of the carry.

A. 16 + 16 = 3 6

5 or more in the 1s place will give you a CARRY. The 10s place will go UP ONE.

If the 1s place number is 5-9 add one more to the tens place

#1 Check if the 1s place digit is 5 or more

#2 Add the TENS place FIRST, but add one if the tens place number is 5 or more

#3 Double the ONES place number, but just write the last digit (1s place)

Double the following numbers by going LEFT to RIGHT

1. 28 + 28 = ☐
2. 34 + 34 = ☐
3. 18 + 18 = ☐
4. 46 + 46 = ☐
5. 27 + 27 = ☐
6. 19 + 19 = ☐
7. 35 + 35 = ☐
8. 47 + 47 = ☐
9. 42 + 42 = ☐

10. 17 + 17 = ☐
11. 26 + 26 = ☐
12. 44 + 44 = ☐
13. 15 + 15 = ☐
14. 41 + 41 = ☐
15. 32 + 32 = ☐
16. 28 + 28 = ☐
17. 29 + 29 = ☐
18. 137 + 137 = ☐

30

Doubling Three-Digit Numbers

Double the following numbers by going LEFT to RIGHT

1. 178 + 178 =

Does the 10s place have a carry?   y   n

add the 100s place
add 1 more if a carry → ☐ ☐ ☐   LAST digit only   LAST digit only

Does the 1s place have a carry?   y   n

add the 10s place
add 1 more if a carry

add the ONES place
LAST digit only

3. 346 + 346 =

Does the 10s place have a carry?   y   n

add the 100s place
add 1 more if a carry → ☐ ☐ ☐   LAST digit only   LAST digit only

Does the 1s place have a carry?   y   n

add the 10s place
add 1 more if a carry

add the ONES place
LAST digit only

2. 287 + 287 =

Does the 10s place have a carry?   y   n

add the 100s place
add 1 more if a carry → ☐ ☐ ☐   LAST digit only   LAST digit only

Does the 1s place have a carry?   y   n

add the 10s place
add 1 more if a carry

add the ONES place
LAST digit only

4. 465 + 465 =

Does the 10s place have a carry?   y   n

add the 100s place
add 1 more if a carry → ☐ ☐ ☐   LAST digit only   LAST digit only

Does the 1s place have a carry?   y   n

add the 10s place
add 1 more if a carry

add the ONES place
LAST digit only

Try doubling these numbers mentally

5. 1 7 6
↓ ↓ ↓
☐ ☐ ☐

6. 4 1 8
↓ ↓ ↓
☐ ☐ ☐

7. 2 9 7
↓ ↓ ↓
☐ ☐ ☐

Doubling Practice

	Double the following numbers

1. 15 + 15 = ☐

2. 35 + 35 = ☐

3. 17 + 17 = ☐

4. 37 + 37 = ☐

5. 19 + 19 = ☐

6. 21 + 21 = ☐

7. 16 + 16 = ☐

8. 36 + 36 = ☐

9. 18 + 18 = ☐

10. 28 + 28 = ☐

Add the 100s first →   Add the 32s together ↙   100 + 100 32 + 32

11. 132 + 132 = ☐

Add the hundreds first   Add the 15s together   200 + 200 15 + 15

12. 215 + 215 = ☐

13. 127 + 127 = ☐

14. 346 + 346 = ☐

15. 138 + 138 = ☐

16. 419 + 419 = ☐

17. 345 + 345 = ☐

18. 243 + 243 = ☐

19. 428 + 428 = ☐

20. 349 + 349 = ☐

Adding Even and Odd Numbers

if both are the same, you get an even number		if one is even and the other is odd, you get an odd number	
Even + Even = EVEN	2 + 6 = 8	Even + Odd = ODD	2 + 3 = 5
	E + E = E		E + O = O
Odd + Odd = EVEN	3 + 7 = 10	Odd + Even = ODD	5 + 2 = 7
	O + O = E		O + E = O

Put "E" for EVEN and "O" for ODD and find the sums

1. 5 + 7 = ☐

☐ ☐ ☐

PUT "E" OR "O" FOR EVEN AND ODD HERE!

2. 4 + 1 = ☐

☐ ☐ ☐

3. 11 + 6 = ☐

☐ ☐ ☐

4. 1 + 7 = ☐

☐ ☐ ☐

5. 9 + 9 = ☐

☐ ☐ ☐

6. 1 + 5 = ☐

☐ ☐ ☐

7. 9 + 1 = ☐

☐ ☐ ☐

8. 7 + 7 = ☐

☐ ☐ ☐

9. 7 + 7 + 7 = ☐

☐ ☐ ☐ ☐

33

Double the Between Number

Example

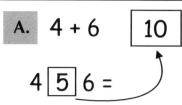

A. 4 + 6 → [10]

4 [5] 6 =

Double the between number — The between number is 5 — Two times 5 is 10

Every time you add it's the same as double the middle

Find the between (middle) number and double it

1. 2 + 4

2 [ ] 4 = [ ]

Double

5. 9 + 7

9 [ ] 7 = [ ]

Double

9. 10 + 12

10 [ ] 12 = [ ]

Double

2. 5 + 7

5 [ ] 7 = [ ]

Double

6. 11 + 9

11 [ ] 9 = [ ]

Double

10. 13 + 15

13 [ ] 15 = [ ]

Double

3. 6 + 8

6 [ ] 8 = [ ]

Double

7. 13 + 11

13 [ ] 11 = [ ]

Double

11. 29 + 31

29 [ ] 31 = [ ]

Double

4. 5 + 3

5 [ ] 3 = [ ]

Double

8. 24 + 26

24 [ ] 26 = [ ]

Double

12. 15 + 17

15 [ ] 17 = [ ]

Double

Double the Between Number

1. 14 + 16

14 ☐ 16 = ☐
Double

2. 16 + 18

16 ☐ 18 = ☐
Double

WHEN BOTH NUMBERS ARE INCREASED BY 2, WHAT HAPPENS TO THE SUM?

3. 22 + 24

22 ☐ 24 = ☐

4. 24 + 26

24 ☐ 26 = ☐

5. 12 + 14

12 ☐ 14 = ☐

6. 33 + 35

33 ☐ 35 = ☐

7. 17 + 19

17 ☐ 19 = ☐

8. 19 + 21

19 ☐ 21 = ☐

9. 36 + 38

36 ☐ 38 = ☐

10. 25 + 27

25 ☐ 27 = ☐

11. 42 + 44

42 ☐ 44 = ☐

12. 47 + 49

47 ☐ 49 = ☐

Double the Between Number

1. 12 + 14

12 ☐ 14 = ☐

Double

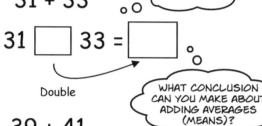

WHAT DO YOU NOTICE ABOUT THE MIDDLE NUMBER AND THE MEAN (AVERAGE)?

2. 31 + 33

31 ☐ 33 = ☐

Double

WHAT CONCLUSION CAN YOU MAKE ABOUT ADDING AVERAGES (MEANS)?

3. 39 + 41

39 ☐ 41 = ☐

4. 55 + 57

55 ☐ 57 = ☐

5. 44 + 46

44 ☐ 46 = ☐

6. 27 + 29

27 ☐ 29 = ☐

7. 85 + 87

85 ☐ 87 = ☐

8. 37 + 39

37 ☐ 39 = ☐

9. 25 + 23

25 ☐ 23 = ☐

10. 32 + 34

32 ☐ 34 = ☐

11. 28 + 26

28 ☐ 26 = ☐

12. 46 + 48

46 ☐ 48 = ☐

Halving Numbers

1. 8 → [ ]

cut the number in half
(divide by 2)

2. 12 → [ ]

3. 10 → [ ]

4. 14 → [ ]

5. 18 → [ ]

6. 16 → [ ]

7. 22 → [ ]

8. 66 → [ ]

9. 44 → [ ]

10. 28 → [ ]

11. 24 → [ ]

12. 240 → [ ]

13. 180 → [ ]

14. 220 → [ ]

15. 460 → [ ]

16. 880 → [ ]

17. 882 → [ ]

18. 260 → [ ]

19. 840 → [ ]

20. 682 → [ ]

Halving Numbers

1. 18 ⟶ ☐

   cut the number in half
   (divide by 2)

2. 22 ⟶ ☐

3. 26 ⟶ ☐

4. 30 ⟶ ☐

5. 28 ⟶ ☐

6. 34 ⟶ ☐

7. 42 ⟶ ☐

8. 64 ⟶ ☐

9. 36 ⟶ ☐

10. 38 ⟶ ☐

11. 68 ⟶ ☐

12. 46 ⟶ ☐

13. 42 ⟶ ☐

14. 32 ⟶ ☐

15. 70 ⟶ ☐

16. 90 ⟶ ☐

17. 150 ⟶ ☐

18. 120 ⟶ ☐

19. 240 ⟶ ☐

20. 1050 ⟶ ☐

Halving Numbers

Cut the following numbers in half

1. 16 → ☐

cut the number in half
(divide by 2)

2. 12 → ☐

3. 14 → ☐

4. 18 → ☐

5. 24 → ☐

6. 28 → ☐

7. 46 → ☐

8. 64 → ☐

9. 32 → ☐

10. 34 → ☐

11. 264 → ☐

12. 428 → ☐

13. 646 → ☐

14. 82 → ☐

15. 22 → ☐

16. 68 → ☐

17. 206 → ☐

18. 408 → ☐

19. 614 → ☐

20. 812 → ☐

39

Mixed Review

Add the following close numbers

1. 6 + 6 = ☐

6 + 7 = ☐

2. 8 + 8 = ☐

8 + 9 = ☐

3. 7 + 7 = ☐

7 + 8 = ☐

Add numbers by making 10s

4. 8 + 5

8 + ☐ + ☐ = ☐

= 10

5. 7 + 4

7 + ☐ + ☐ = ☐

= 10

6. 9 + 3

9 + ☐ + ☐ = ☐

= 10

Add the original numbers, add the additional tens, solve the new problems

7. 9 + 4 = ☐ 19 + 14

how much more
is this? ☐

19 + 14 = ☐

8. 8 + 7 = ☐ 28 + 27

how much more
is this? ☐

28 + 27 = ☐

Double the following numbers

9. 14 → ☐

10. 17 → ☐

11. 19 → ☐

Cut the following numbers in half

12. 36 → ☐

13. 52 → ☐

13. 76 → ☐

Halving Numbers when the 10s Digit is Odd

Method #1: Breaking up the number into 10s and 1s

Example

A.

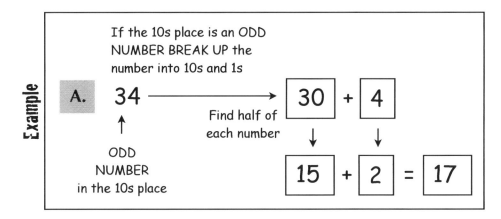

If the 10s place is an ODD NUMBER BREAK UP the number into 10s and 1s

34 → 30 + 4

↑ ODD NUMBER in the 10s place

Find half of each number

15 + 2 = 17

Cut the following numbers in half

Value of 10s place digit   1s

1. 52 → $\boxed{50}$ + $\boxed{}$

cut each number in half $\boxed{}$ + $\boxed{}$ = $\boxed{}$

4. 98 → $\boxed{}$ + $\boxed{}$

cut each number in half $\boxed{}$ + $\boxed{}$ = $\boxed{}$

2. 38 → $\boxed{}$ + $\boxed{}$

cut each number in half $\boxed{}$ + $\boxed{}$ = $\boxed{}$

5. 74 → $\boxed{}$ + $\boxed{}$

cut each number in half $\boxed{}$ + $\boxed{}$ = $\boxed{}$

3. 76 → $\boxed{}$ + $\boxed{}$

cut each number in half $\boxed{}$ + $\boxed{}$ = $\boxed{}$

6. 58 → $\boxed{}$ + $\boxed{}$

$\boxed{}$ + $\boxed{}$ = $\boxed{}$

Halving Numbers when the 10s Digit is Odd

Cut the following numbers in half by breaking up the numbers into 10s and 1s

Value of 10s place digit   1s

1. 34 → $\boxed{30}$ + $\boxed{}$

cut each number in half $\boxed{}$ + $\boxed{}$ = $\boxed{}$

6. 78 → $\boxed{}$ + $\boxed{}$

cut each number in half $\boxed{}$ + $\boxed{}$ = $\boxed{}$

2. 72 → $\boxed{}$ + $\boxed{}$

cut each number in half $\boxed{}$ + $\boxed{}$ = $\boxed{}$

7. 54 → $\boxed{}$ + $\boxed{}$

cut each number in half $\boxed{}$ + $\boxed{}$ = $\boxed{}$

3. 38 → $\boxed{}$ + $\boxed{}$

cut each number in half $\boxed{}$ + $\boxed{}$ = $\boxed{}$

8. 96 → $\boxed{}$ + $\boxed{}$

cut each number in half $\boxed{}$ + $\boxed{}$ = $\boxed{}$

4. 92 → $\boxed{}$ + $\boxed{}$

cut each number in half $\boxed{}$ + $\boxed{}$ = $\boxed{}$

9. 52 → $\boxed{}$ + $\boxed{}$

cut each number in half $\boxed{}$ + $\boxed{}$ = $\boxed{}$

5. 36 → $\boxed{}$ + $\boxed{}$

cut each number in half $\boxed{}$ + $\boxed{}$ = $\boxed{}$

10. 74 → $\boxed{}$ + $\boxed{}$

cut each number in half $\boxed{}$ + $\boxed{}$ = $\boxed{}$

Halving Numbers with Odd Digits

Method #1: Breaking up the number into 100s, 10s and 1s

Example

A. 534 →

	100s		10s		1s		
	500	+	30	+	4		

cut each number in half

250	+	15	+	2	=	282

Cut the following numbers in half by breaking up the numbers into 100s, 10s and 1s

1. 356 →
□ + □ + □

(100s 10s 1s)

cut each number in half
□ + □ + □

= □

4. 586 →
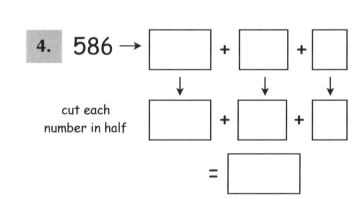

2. 278 →
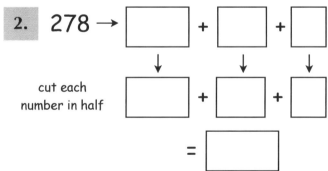

5. 372 →
□ + □ + □

cut each number in half
□ + □ + □

= □

3. 732 →
□ + □ + □

cut each number in half
□ + □ + □

= □

6. 958 →
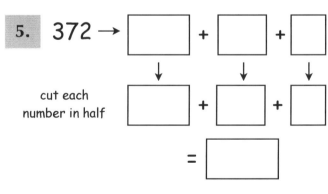

© Peter Wise, 2016

43

Halving Numbers when the 10s Digit is Odd

The Subtract 1, Insert 1 Trick

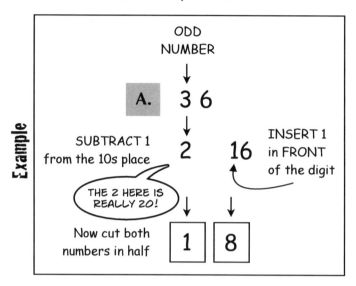

Example

A.

ODD NUMBER

3 6

SUBTRACT 1 from the 10s place

2   16   INSERT 1 in FRONT of the digit

THE 2 HERE IS REALLY 20!

Now cut both numbers in half

1   8

Cut the following numbers in half

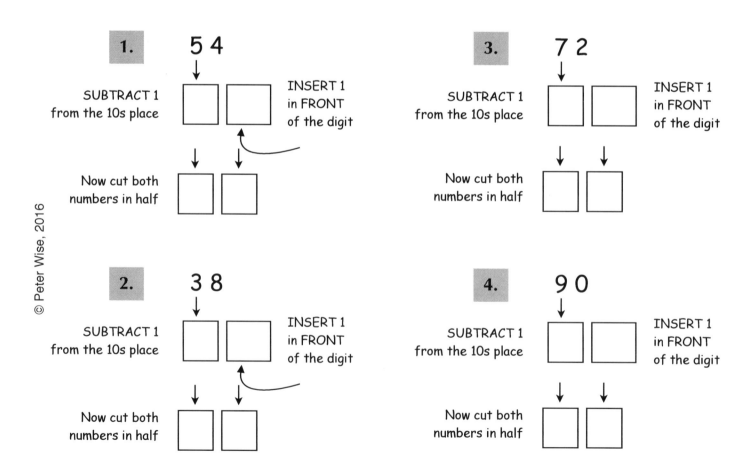

1. 5 4

SUBTRACT 1 from the 10s place

INSERT 1 in FRONT of the digit

Now cut both numbers in half

3. 7 2

SUBTRACT 1 from the 10s place

INSERT 1 in FRONT of the digit

Now cut both numbers in half

2. 3 8

SUBTRACT 1 from the 10s place

INSERT 1 in FRONT of the digit

Now cut both numbers in half

4. 9 0

SUBTRACT 1 from the 10s place

INSERT 1 in FRONT of the digit

Now cut both numbers in half

Intro to Short Division

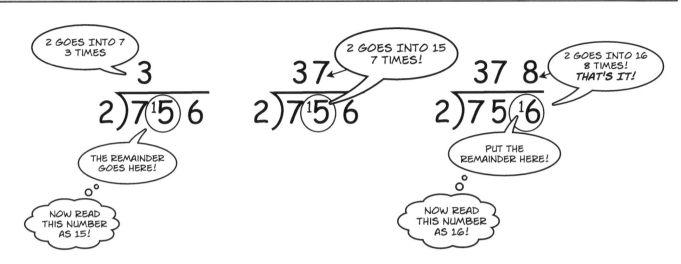

Solve the following problems using SHORT DIVISION

Circles on the numbers are helpful for now, but you won't usually have them

1. 2⟌7③④

2. 2⟌5③⑥

3. 2⟌3⑨⓪

4. 2⟌9③⑨②

5. 2⟌8⑨⑧

6. 2⟌7⑥⓪

7. 2⟌5⑦⑨③④

8. 2⟌8③②⑦⑥

Short Division Practice

1. $2\overline{)9⃝8⃝6}$

2. $2\overline{)3⃝4⃝0}$

3. $2\overline{)7⃝0⃝3⃝4}$

4. $2\overline{)8⃝1⃝0⃝6}$

5. $2\overline{)1⃝7⃝6⃝4}$

6. $2\overline{)5⃝9⃝5}\ \overline{2}$ ← remainder

7. $2\overline{)6⃝2⃝9}\ \overline{2}$ ← remainder

8. $2\overline{)8⃝0⃝3⃝7}\ \overline{2}$

9. $2\overline{)3⃝0⃝0⃝1}\ \overline{2}$

10. $2\overline{)9⃝7⃝3⃝5}\ \overline{2}$

Short Division Practice

Solve the following problems using SHORT DIVISION

1. 2)9 ③ ⑧

2. 2)7 ① ②

3. 2)6 ⓪ ③ ④

4. 2)8 ① ⓪ ⑥

5. 2)3 ⑤ ⑨ ⑦   ‾2 ← remainder

6. 2)5 ② ③   ‾2 ← remainder

7. 2)8 ⑦ ⑤   ‾2 ← remainder

8. 2)6 ⓪ ① ①   ‾2 ← remainder

9. 2)1 ⑨ ③ ⑦   ‾2 ← remainder

10. 2)7 ⑧ ⑤ ⑨   ‾2 ← remainder

WHAT DO YOU NOTICE WHEN THE NUMBER 2 DIVIDES INTO ODD NUMBERS?

47

Short Division Practice

Solve the following problems using SHORT DIVISION

1. 2)5②⓪

6. 2)9⑨7 ←— remainder $^{\overline{2}}$

2. 2)8③④

7. 2)3⑥① $^{\overline{2}}$

3. 2)5⑨②⑧

8. 2)4⑦③⑨ $^{\overline{2}}$

4. 2)9⑤⑧②

9. 2)3⑤⑦⑤ $^{\overline{2}}$

5. 2)3⓪④⑤ ←— remainder $^{\overline{2}}$

10. 2)7①⑧③ $^{\overline{2}}$

Short Division Practice

Solve the following problems using SHORT DIVISION

1. $5 \overline{)\, 6\,⑦\,⑤}$

2. $5 \overline{)\, 8\,①\,⑤}$

3. $5 \overline{)\, 3\,⑤\,⑨\,⓪}$

4. $5 \overline{)\, 7\,⓪\,⓪\,⑤}$

5. $5 \overline{)\, 9\,②\,④\,⑤}$

6. $5 \overline{)\, 8\,⑨\,⑥}$ $\overline{5}$ ← remainder

7. $5 \overline{)\, 4\,⑦\,③}$ $\overline{5}$ ← remainder

8. $5 \overline{)\, 9\,⑥\,⑧\,⑦}$ $\overline{5}$ ← remainder

9. $5 \overline{)\, 6\,②\,⑧\,③}$ $\overline{5}$ ← remainder

10. $5 \overline{)\, 7\,⑤\,③\,⑨}$ $\overline{5}$ ← remainder

Short Division Practice

Solve the following problems using SHORT DIVISION

1. 5 ⟌ 7 ③ ⑤

6. 5 ⟌ 5 ② ⑦ $\overline{5}$ ← remainder

2. 5 ⟌ 9 ② ⑤

7. 5 ⟌ 6 ⑨ ⑥ $\overline{5}$ ← remainder

3. 5 ⟌ 6 ⑧ ⓪ ⑤

8. 5 ⟌ 2 8 7 1 $\overline{5}$ ← remainder

4. 5 ⟌ 2 2 6 0

9. 5 ⟌ 8 7 9 2 $\overline{5}$ ← remainder

5. 5 ⟌ 8 0 1 5

10. 5 ⟌ 9 1 6 2 $\overline{5}$ ← remainder

50

Short Division Practice

1. $3\overline{)4\ 1\ 4}$

2. $4\overline{)5\ 7\ 6}$

3. $2\overline{)7\ 3\ 9\ 8}$

4. $3\overline{)7\ 1\ 8}$ $\overline{3}$ ← remainder

5. $2\overline{)9\ 5\ 3\ 1}$ $\overline{2}$ ← remainder

6. $5\overline{)8\ 4\ 3\ 9}$ $\overline{5}$ ← remainder

7. $3\overline{)5\ 3\ 4\ 7}$ $\overline{3}$ ← remainder

8. $4\overline{)8\ 0\ 6\ 3}$ $\overline{4}$ ← remainder

9. $5\overline{)9\ 1\ 4\ 8}$ $\overline{5}$

10. $3\overline{)8\ 0\ 2\ 4}$ $\overline{3}$

© Peter Wise, 2016

51

Adding Nines

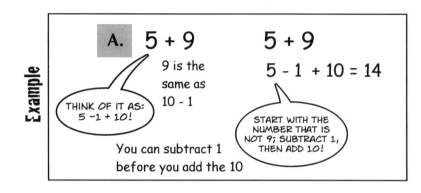

Example

| A. | 5 + 9 | 5 + 9 |

9 is the same as 10 - 1

THINK OF IT AS: 5 −1 + 10!

You can subtract 1 before you add the 10

5 - 1 + 10 = 14

START WITH THE NUMBER THAT IS NOT 9; SUBTRACT 1, THEN ADD 10!

Adding 9 is the same as "Subtract 1, add 10"

Add nines by SUBTRACTING 1 and ADDING 10

1. 8 + 9

Start here → -1 = ☐ + 10 = ☐

2. 6 + 9

-1 = ☐ + 10 = ☐

3. 4 + 9

-1 = ☐ + 10 = ☐

4. 7 + 9

-1 = ☐ + 10 = ☐

5. 3 + 9

-1 = ☐ + 10 = ☐

6. 12 + 9

-1 = ☐ + 10 = ☐

7. 27 + 9

-1 = ☐ + 10 = ☐

8. 14 + 9

-1 = ☐ + 10 = ☐

9. 36 + 9

-1 = ☐ + 10 = ☐

10. 75 + 9

-1 = ☐ + 10 = ☐

Adding Nines

Example

A. $14 + 9 = 23$

Add 10 | 24

Subtract 1 | 23

YOU CAN ALSO SWITCH THE ORDER!

Idea behind this

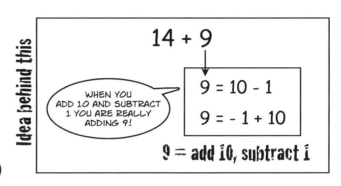

$14 + 9$

$9 = 10 - 1$

$9 = -1 + 10$

WHEN YOU ADD 10 AND SUBTRACT 1 YOU ARE REALLY ADDING 9!

9 = add 10, subtract 1

Solve the following addition problems by adding 10 and subtracting 1

1. 5 + 9

+ 10 ☐

- 1 ☐ ← answer

2. 13 + 9

+ 10 ☐

- 1 ☐ ← answer

3. 16 + 9

+ 10 ☐

- 1 ☐

4. 38 + 9

+ 10 ☐

- 1 ☐

5. 27 + 9

+ 10 ☐

- 1 ☐

6. 56 + 9

+ 10 ☐

- 1 ☐

7. 38 + 9

+ 10 ☐

- 1 ☐

8. 72 + 9

+ 10 ☐

- 1 ☐

9. 569 + 9

+ 10 ☐

- 1 ☐

10. 842 + 9

+ 10 ☐

- 1 ☐

11. 236 + 9

+ 10 ☐

- 1 ☐

12. 6,775 + 9

+ 10 ☐

- 1 ☐

Subtracting Nines

Example

A. $15 - 9 = 6$

Subtract 10 | 5
Add 1 | 6

YOU CAN ALSO SWITCH THE ORDER!

Idea behind this

$15 - 9$

WHEN YOU SUBTRACT 10 AND ADD 1 YOU ARE REALLY SUBTRACTING 9!

$-9 = -10 + 1$

$-9 = +1 - 10$

$-9 =$ subtract 10, add 1

Question: How do you remember when to (+10 -1) or (-10 + 1)?

Answer: If you are SUBTRACTING 9, subtract the LARGER number (10)

Solve the following subtraction problems by subtracting 10 and adding 1

1. $27 - 9$
- 10 [ ]
+ 1 [ ] ← answer

5. $16 - 9$
- 10 [ ]
+ 1 [ ]

9. $245 - 9$
- 10 [ ]
+ 1 [ ]

2. $14 - 9$
- 10 [ ]
+ 1 [ ] ← answer

6. $48 - 9$
- 10 [ ]
+ 1 [ ]

10. $872 - 9$
- 10 [ ]
+ 1 [ ]

3. $59 - 9$
- 10 [ ]
+ 1 [ ]

7. $73 - 9$
- 10 [ ]
+ 1 [ ]

11. $481 - 9$
- 10 [ ]
+ 1 [ ]

4. $17 - 9$
- 10 [ ]
+ 1 [ ]

8. $63 - 9$
- 10 [ ]
+ 1 [ ]

12. $4,985 - 9$
- 10 [ ]
+ 1 [ ]

Mixed Review

Cut the following numbers in half

1. 58 ⟶ 10s [ ] + 1s [ ]

   cut each number in half [ ] + [ ] = [ ]

2. 94 ⟶ [ ] + [ ]

   cut each number in half [ ] + [ ] = [ ]

Cut the following numbers in half by breaking up the numbers into 100s, 10s and 1s

3. 738 ⟶ 100s [ ] + 10s [ ] + 1s [ ]

   cut each number in half [ ] + [ ] + [ ]

   = [ ]

4. 394 ⟶ [ ] + [ ] + [ ]

   cut each number in half [ ] + [ ] + [ ]

   = [ ]

Add nines by SUBTRACTING 1 and ADDING 10

5. 7 + 9
   ↓
   -1 = [ ] + 10 = [ ]

6. 24 + 9
   ↓
   -1 = [ ] + 10 = [ ]

Solve the following subtraction problems by subtracting 10 and adding 1

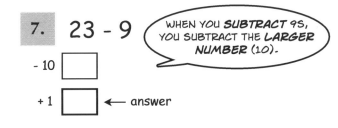

7. 23 - 9   *WHEN YOU SUBTRACT 9S, YOU SUBTRACT THE LARGER NUMBER (10).*

   - 10 [ ]

   + 1 [ ] ← answer

8. 34 - 9

   - 10 [ ]

   + 1 [ ] ← answer

9. 462 - 9

   - 10 [ ]

   + 1 [ ] ← answer

55

Adding Eights

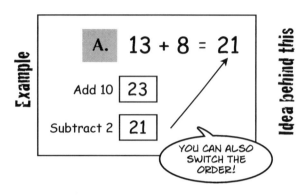

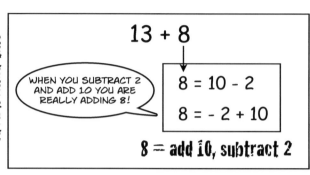

Solve the following addition problems by adding 10 and subtracting 2

1. 7 + 8

+ 10 [ ]

− 2 [ ] ← answer

2. 5 + 8

+ 10 [ ]

− 2 [ ] ← answer

3. 13 + 8

+ 10 [ ]

− 2 [ ]

4. 14 + 8

+ 10 [ ]

− 2 [ ]

5. 26 + 8

+ 10 [ ]

− 2 [ ]

6. 54 + 8

+ 10 [ ]

− 2 [ ]

7. 73 + 8

+ 10 [ ]

− 2 [ ]

8. 89 + 8

+ 10 [ ]

− 2 [ ]

9. 235 + 8

+ 10 [ ]

− 2 [ ]

10. 979 + 8

+ 10 [ ]

− 2 [ ]

11. 617 + 8

+ 10 [ ]

− 2 [ ]

12. 2,786 + 8

+ 10 [ ]

− 2 [ ]

56

Subtracting Eights

Example

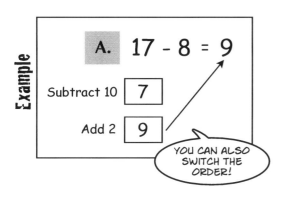

A. 17 - 8 = 9

Subtract 10 [7]

Add 2 [9]

YOU CAN ALSO SWITCH THE ORDER!

Idea behind this

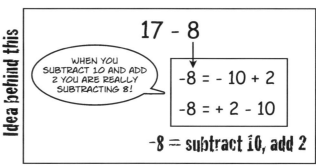

17 - 8

WHEN YOU SUBTRACT 10 AND ADD 2 YOU ARE REALLY SUBTRACTING 8!

-8 = -10 + 2

-8 = +2 - 10

-8 = subtract 10, add 2

Solve the following subtraction problems by subtracting 10 and adding 2

1. 11 - 8

- 10 [ ]

+ 2 [ ] ← answer

2. 13 - 8

- 10 [ ]

+ 2 [ ] ← answer

3. 15 - 8

- 10 [ ]

+ 2 [ ]

4. 14 - 8

- 10 [ ]

+ 2 [ ]

5. 27 - 8

- 10 [ ]

+ 2 [ ]

6. 25 - 8

- 10 [ ]

+ 2 [ ]

7. 21 - 8

- 10 [ ]

+ 2 [ ]

8. 32 - 8

- 10 [ ]

+ 2 [ ]

9. 356 - 8

- 10 [ ]

+ 2 [ ]

10. 261 - 8

- 10 [ ]

+ 2 [ ]

11. 742 - 8

- 10 [ ]

+ 2 [ ]

12. 9,857 - 8

- 10 [ ]

+ 2 [ ]

Adding Eighteens

Example

A. $17 + 18 = 21$

Add 20 $\boxed{37}$

Subtract 2 $\boxed{35}$

YOU CAN ALSO SWITCH THE ORDER!

Idea behind this

another way to think of 18

TO ADD 18 JUST ADD 20 AND THEN SUBTRACT 2!

$$18 = 20 - 2$$
$$18 = -2 + 20$$

add 20, subtract 2

Pattern: UP a 20, DOWN 2

Solve the following addition problems by adding 20 and subtracting 2

1. $3 + 18$

+ 20 ☐

− 2 ☐ ← answer

5. $59 + 18$

+ 20 ☐

− 2 ☐

9. $469 + 18$

+ 20 ☐

− 2 ☐

2. $7 + 18$

+ 20 ☐

− 2 ☐ ← answer

6. $27 + 18$

+ 20 ☐

− 2 ☐

10. $139 + 18$

+ 20 ☐

− 2 ☐

3. $14 + 18$

+ 20 ☐

− 2 ☐

7. $63 + 18$

+ 20 ☐

− 2 ☐

11. $827 + 18$

+ 20 ☐

− 2 ☐

4. $36 + 18$

+ 20 ☐

− 2 ☐

8. $97 + 18$

+ 20 ☐

− 2 ☐

12. $3,684 + 18$

+ 20 ☐

− 2 ☐

58

+ 19 = Up a 2o, Down a One

Example

A. $47 + 19 =$ $47 + 20 =$ [ ] $- 1 =$ [ ]

(20 - 1)

+ 19 IS REALLY
"UP TWO TENS,
DOWN A ONE!"

same as + 19!

Solve these + 19 problems by adding 20, then subtracting 1

1. $26 + 19 =$ [ ] $- 1 =$ [ ]   now your answer is the same as if you had added 19 in the first place!

    add 26 + 20

2. $77 + 19 =$ [ ] $- 1 =$ [ ]   7. $79 + 19 =$ [ ]

    add 77 + 20   add 20 and then subtract 1

3. $41 + 19 =$ [ ] $- 1 =$ [ ]   8. $28 + 19 =$ [ ]

    + 20

4. $83 + 19 =$ [ ] $- 1 =$ [ ]   9. $35 + 19 =$ [ ]

5. $59 + 19 =$ [ ] $- 1 =$ [ ]   10. $62 + 19 =$ [ ]

6. $16 + 19 =$ [ ] $- 1 =$ [ ]   11. $74 + 19 =$ [ ]

59

Adding Nineteens

Example

A. 35 + 19 = 54

Add 20 | 55

Subtract 1 | 54

YOU CAN ALSO SWITCH THE ORDER!

Idea behind this

another way to think of 19

TO ADD 19 JUST ADD 20 AND THEN SUBTRACT 1!

19 = 20 - 1

19 = - 1 + 20

add 20, subtract 1

Solve the following addition problems by adding 20 and subtracting 1

1. 7 + 19

+ 20 [ ]

- 1 [ ] ← answer

2. 3 + 19

+ 20 [ ]

- 1 [ ] ← answer

3. 58 + 19

+ 20 [ ]

- 1 [ ]

4. 16 + 19

+ 20 [ ]

- 1 [ ]

5. 49 + 19

+ 20 [ ]

- 1 [ ]

6. 75 + 19

+ 20 [ ]

- 1 [ ]

7. 82 + 19

+ 20 [ ]

- 1 [ ]

8. 127 + 19

+ 20 [ ]

- 1 [ ]

9. 324 + 19

+ 20 [ ]

- 1 [ ]

10. 563 + 19

+ 20 [ ]

- 1 [ ]

11. 795 + 19

+ 20 [ ]

- 1 [ ]

12. 2,386 + 19

+ 20 [ ]

- 1 [ ]

+ 99 = Up a 100, Down a One

Example

A. 47 + 99 =   47 + 100 = ☐ 147   – 1 = ☐ 146

(100 – 1)

99 IS THE SAME AS 100–1!

same as + 99!

Solve these + 99 problems by adding 100, then subtracting 1

1. 37 + 99 = ☐ – 1 = ☐   now your answer is the same as if you had added 99 in the first place!
   + 100

2. 62 + 99 = ☐ – 1 = ☐   7. 6148 + 99 = ☐
   + 100

3. 735 + 99 = ☐ – 1 = ☐   8. 3875 + 99 = ☐
   + 100

4. 316 + 99 = ☐ – 1 = ☐   9. 99 + 1763 = ☐

5. 99 + 643 = ☐ – 1 = ☐   10. 99 + 8210 = ☐

6. 99 + 824 = ☐ – 1 = ☐   11. 5650 + 99 = ☐

Mixed Review

Cut the following numbers in half, using the "Minus 1, Insert 1" Trick

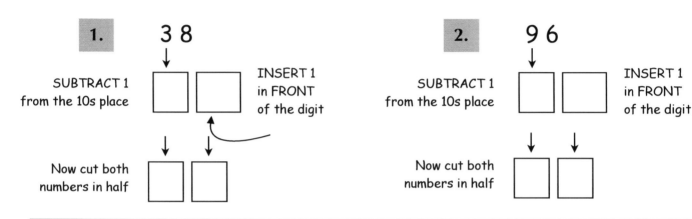

1.   3 8

SUBTRACT 1 from the 10s place   [ ] [ ]   INSERT 1 in FRONT of the digit

Now cut both numbers in half   [ ] [ ]

2.   9 6

SUBTRACT 1 from the 10s place   [ ] [ ]   INSERT 1 in FRONT of the digit

Now cut both numbers in half   [ ] [ ]

ONE MORE FOR THE FIVES: Find the sums of the following numbers

[ ] add the 5s

3.   15 + 35 = [ ]

[ ] add the tens place

[ ] add the 5s

4.   45 + 25 = [ ]

[ ] add the tens place

Solve the following addition problems by adding 10 and subtracting 2

5.   5 + 8

+ 10 [ ]

- 2 [ ] ← answer

6.   27 + 8

+ 10 [ ]

- 2 [ ]

7.   354 + 8

+ 10 [ ]

- 2 [ ]

Solve the following addition problems by adding 20 and subtracting 1

8.   6 + 19

+ 20 [ ]

- 1 [ ] ← answer

9.   38 + 19

+ 20 [ ]

- 1 [ ]

10.   627 + 19

+ 20 [ ]

- 1 [ ]

+/- Same Amounts Trick

Example

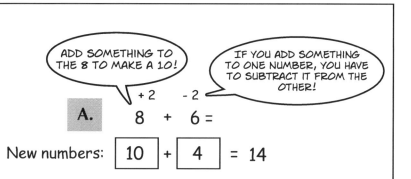

ADD SOMETHING TO THE 8 TO MAKE A 10!

IF YOU ADD SOMETHING TO ONE NUMBER, YOU HAVE TO SUBTRACT IT FROM THE OTHER!

A. +2   -2
8   +   6 =

New numbers: [10] + [4] = 14

Add to the first number to round up, then subtract from the other number

1. +[2] -[ ]
8 + 5 =

New numbers: [ ] + [ ] = [ ]

6. +[ ] -[ ]
18 + 6 =

[ ] + [ ] = [ ]

HOW MUCH DO YOU NEED TO ADD TO MAKE 20?

2. +[ ] -[ ]
9 + 8 =

[ ] + [ ] = [ ]

7. +[ ] -[ ]
17 + 7 =

[ ] + [ ] = [ ]

3. +[ ] -[ ]
8 + 7 =

[ ] + [ ] = [ ]

8. +[ ] -[ ]
16 + 9 =

[ ] + [ ] = [ ]

4. +[ ] -[ ]
7 + 9 =

[ ] + [ ] = [ ]

9. +[ ] -[ ]
19 + 7 =

[ ] + [ ] = [ ]

HOW MUCH DO YOU NEED TO MAKE 90?

5. +[ ] -[ ]
86 + 6 =

[ ] + [ ] = [ ]

10. +[ ] -[ ]
119 + 8 =

[ ] + [ ] = [ ]

+/- Same Amounts Trick

Example

YOU ADD 1 TO 49 TO ROUND UP AND MAKE A NUMBER EASIER TO ADD WITH!

YOU CAN ADD ANY AMOUNT TO ONE NUMBER, AS LONG AS YOU SUBTRACT IT FROM THE OTHER NUMBER!

A. $+1$ -1

49 + 35 =

New numbers: 50 + 34 = 84

Add to the first number to round up, then subtract from the other number

1. $+\boxed{1}$ $-\boxed{}$

39 + 26 =

New numbers: ☐ + ☐ = ☐

2. $+\boxed{}$ $-\boxed{}$

58 + 35 =

☐ + ☐ = ☐

3. $+\boxed{}$ $-\boxed{}$

89 + 27 =

☐ + ☐ = ☐

4. $+\boxed{}$ $-\boxed{}$

17 + 45 =

☐ + ☐ = ☐

5. $+\boxed{}$ $-\boxed{}$

119 + 54 =

☐ + ☐ = ☐

6. $+\boxed{}$ $-\boxed{}$

38 + 13 =

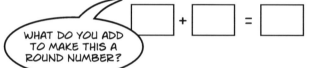

WHAT DO YOU ADD TO MAKE THIS A ROUND NUMBER?

☐ + ☐ = ☐

7. $+\boxed{}$ $-\boxed{}$

56 + 35 =

☐ + ☐ = ☐

8. $+\boxed{}$ $-\boxed{}$

18 + 68 =

☐ + ☐ = ☐

9. $+\boxed{}$ $-\boxed{}$

57 + 24 =

☐ + ☐ = ☐

10. $+\boxed{}$ $-\boxed{}$

128 + 47 =

☐ + ☐ = ☐

+/- Same Amounts Trick

Example

SUBTRACT 1 TO MAKE A ROUND NUMBER!

DO THE OPPOSITE TO THIS NUMBER!

A.

$$-1 \quad +1$$
$$21 + 47 =$$

New numbers: $\boxed{20} + \boxed{48} = 68$

Subtract from the first number to round down, then add to the other number

1.
$$-\boxed{1} \quad +\boxed{}$$
$$51 + 35 =$$

New numbers: $\boxed{} + \boxed{} = \boxed{}$

6.
$$-\boxed{} \quad +\boxed{}$$
$$22 + 35 =$$

WHAT CAN YOU SUBTRACT TO MAKE THIS AN EASY ROUND NUMBER?

$\boxed{} + \boxed{} = \boxed{}$

2.
$$-\boxed{} \quad +\boxed{}$$
$$11 + 84 =$$

$\boxed{} + \boxed{} = \boxed{}$

7.
$$-\boxed{} \quad +\boxed{}$$
$$12 + 84 =$$

$\boxed{} + \boxed{} = \boxed{}$

3.
$$-\boxed{} \quad +\boxed{}$$
$$71 + 18 =$$

$\boxed{} + \boxed{} = \boxed{}$

8.
$$-\boxed{} \quad +\boxed{}$$
$$52 + 29 =$$

$\boxed{} + \boxed{} = \boxed{}$

4.
$$-\boxed{} \quad +\boxed{}$$
$$61 + 38 =$$

$\boxed{} + \boxed{} = \boxed{}$

9.
$$-\boxed{} \quad +\boxed{}$$
$$22 + 76 =$$

$\boxed{} + \boxed{} = \boxed{}$

5.
$$-\boxed{} \quad +\boxed{}$$
$$121 + 53 =$$

$\boxed{} + \boxed{} = \boxed{}$

10.
$$-\boxed{} \quad +\boxed{}$$
$$132 + 57 =$$

$\boxed{} + \boxed{} = \boxed{}$

65

+/- Same Amounts Trick

Add or subtract in the boxes, then solve these problems mentally

1. $+\Box$ $-\Box$
19 + 17 = $\Box$

2. $-\Box$ $+\Box$
31 + 64 = $\Box$

3. $+\Box$ $-\Box$
49 + 13 = $\Box$

4. $-\Box$ $+\Box$
61 + 38 = $\Box$

5. $-\Box$ $+\Box$
121 + 73 = $\Box$

6. $+\Box$ $-\Box$
258 + 23 = $\Box$

7. $-\Box$ $+\Box$
42 + 35 = $\Box$

8. $+\Box$ $-\Box$
27 + 45 = $\Box$

9. $-\Box$ $+\Box$
52 + 39 = $\Box$

10. $+\Box$ $-\Box$
37 + 26 = $\Box$

11. $-\Box$ $+\Box$
132 + 57 = $\Box$

12. $+\Box$ $-\Box$
118 + 17 = $\Box$

66

Mixed Review

Calculate the tens and the ones; then add them together

1. 7 tens and 56 = ☐

3. 9 tens and 25 = ☐

2. 12 tens and 23 = ☐

4. 14 tens and 57 = ☐

Make 20s and tell how much over 20

5. 17 + 9

17 + ☐ + ☐ = ☐

= 20

6. 16 + 8

16 + ☐ + ☐ = ☐

= 20

Make 50s by finding the missing numbers

7.
```
  1 4
+ 3☐
─────
  5 0
```

8.
```
  2 7
+ 2☐
─────
  5 0
```

9.
```
  3 2
+ ☐
─────
  5 0
```

10.
```
  3 9
+ ☐
─────
  5 0
```

Add to the first number to round up, then subtract from the other number

11. +☐ -☐
7 + 5 =

New numbers: ☐ + ☐ = ☐

12. +☐ -☐
18 + 6 =

☐ + ☐ = ☐

13. +☐ -☐
29 + 8 =

☐ + ☐ = ☐

Solve these + 18 problems by adding 20, then subtracting 2

14. 53 + 18 = ☐ - 2 = ☐

53 + 20

15. 76 + 18 = ☐ - 2 = ☐

76 + 20

Subtracting in Steps

A. $100 - 35 = \boxed{65}$

Example

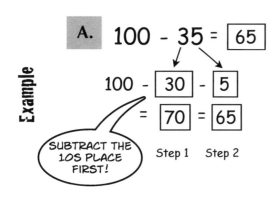

$100 - \boxed{30} - \boxed{5}$

$= \boxed{70} = \boxed{65}$

SUBTRACT THE 10S PLACE FIRST!

Step 1   Step 2

You don't have to subtract numbers all at once!

You can break up subtraction problems into smaller subtraction problems

---

Solve the following subtraction problems by subtracting in steps

1. 100 - 73

$100 - \boxed{70} - \boxed{} = \boxed{}$

2. 100 - 46

$100 - \boxed{} - \boxed{} = \boxed{}$

3. 80 - 19

$80 - \boxed{} - \boxed{} = \boxed{}$

4. 160 - 32

$160 - \boxed{} - \boxed{} = \boxed{}$

5. 180 - 45

$180 - \boxed{} - \boxed{} = \boxed{}$

6. 48 - 25

$48 - \boxed{} - \boxed{} = \boxed{}$

7. 70 - 38

$70 - \boxed{} - \boxed{} = \boxed{}$

8. 200 - 54

$200 - \boxed{} - \boxed{} = \boxed{}$

9. 457 - 25

$457 - \boxed{} - \boxed{} = \boxed{}$

10. 875 - 252

$875 - \boxed{} - \boxed{} - \boxed{} = \boxed{}$

Calculate Mentally

Calculate mentally

11. $5 + 2 + \boxed{} = 10$

12. $2 + 6 + \boxed{} = 10$

13. $12 + 2 + \boxed{} = 20$

14. $3 + 13 + \boxed{} = 20$

Calculate mentally

15. $50 - 8 = \boxed{}$

16. $50 - 18 = \boxed{}$

17. $80 - 4 = \boxed{}$

18. $70 - 21 = \boxed{}$

Add or subtract the following numbers mentally; line them up correctly in your head!

1. $648 + 310 = \boxed{}$

2. $362 + 136 = \boxed{}$

3. $2475 - 300 = \boxed{}$

4. $3000 - 300 + 20 = \boxed{}$

5. $482 - 50 = \boxed{}$

6. $7965 - 500 = \boxed{}$

7. $320 + 60 + 17 = \boxed{}$

8. $7965 - 500 = \boxed{}$

9. $1000 - 420 = \boxed{}$

10. $1000 - 321 = \boxed{}$

Subtracting, Using a Between Number

Example

A. 25 - 17   **#1** Reverse the order   17   25

#2 Pick an easy number between the two numbers.
(Usually it is best to start with the lower number
and go up to the nearest ten.)

Find a middle number
Add the differences between it

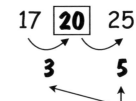

17 **20** 25

3   **5**

#3 Find the difference between the middle number
and the lower and higher numbers

#4 Add these numbers—you're done!   **3 + 5 = 8**
the answer!

25 - 17 = 8

Find a between number and add the differences

---

1. 22 - 16   16 ⬜ 22   ← Reverse the order

Take the lower number, go
up to the nearest 10
put this in the middle box

Number in the middle minus 16 → ⬜ ⬜ ← 22 minus the number in the middle

Add the two numbers above → ⬜

This is the answer to 22 - 16

2. 23 - 14   14 ⬜ 23   ← Reverse the order

Take the lower number, go
up to the nearest 10
put this in the middle box

Number in the middle
minus the lower number → ⬜ ⬜ ← Higher number minus the
number in the middle

Add the two numbers above → ⬜

This is the answer to 23 - 14

70

Subtracting, Using a Between Number

| Find a between number and add the differences |

1. 21 - 13

13 [ ] 21 ← Reverse the order

Take the lower number, go up to the nearest 10 put this in the middle box

Number in the middle minus 13 → [ ]   [ ] ← 21 minus the number in the middle

Add the two numbers above → [ ]

↑
This is the answer to 21 - 13

2. 28 - 11

[ ] [ ] [ ] ← Reverse the order

Take the lower number, go up to the nearest 10 put this in the middle box

Find the difference → [ ]   [ ] ← Find the difference

Add the two numbers above → [ ]

↑
Answer

3. 34 - 16

[ ] [ ] [ ] ← Reverse the order

Take the lower number, go up to the nearest 10 put this in the middle box

Find the difference → [ ]   [ ] ← Find the difference

Add the two numbers above → [ ]

↑
Answer

4. 43 - 18

[ ] [ ] [ ] ← Reverse the order

→ [ ]   [ ] ←

Add the two numbers above → [ ]

↑
Answer

71

Subtracting, Using a Between Number

Find a between number and add the differences

Between number

1. 23 - 17

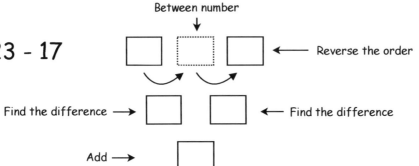

← Reverse the order

Take the lower number, go up to the nearest 10 put this in the middle box

Find the difference →

← Find the difference

Add →

Between number

2. 27 - 18

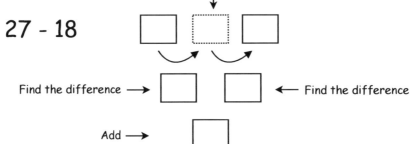

Find the difference →

← Find the difference

Add →

Between number

3. 35 - 19

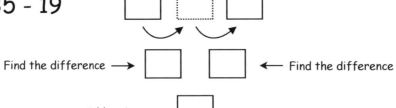

Find the difference →

← Find the difference

Add →

Between number

4. 42 - 27

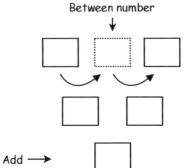

Add →

Subtracting, Using a Between Number

Find a between number and add the differences

1. 62 - 23

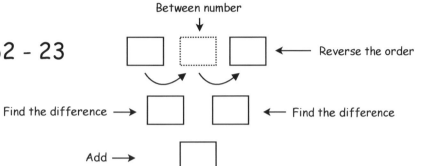

2. 73 - 45

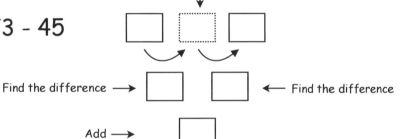

3. 58 - 23

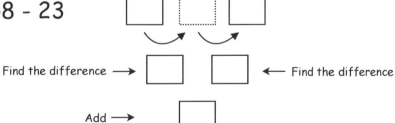

4. 74 - 36

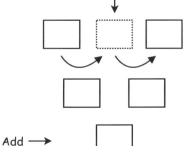

Subtracting, Using Amounts Above & Below 100

Use the number 100 as the between number and add the differences

1. 108 - 94

How far is 108 from 100?   How far is 94 from 100?

☐   ☐

Add the two differences: ☐

2. 120 - 98

How far is 120 from 100?   How far is 98 from 100?

☐   ☐

Add ☐

3. 115 - 88

How far from 100?   How far from 100?

☐   ☐

Add ☐

4. 133 - 89

How far from 100?   How far from 100?

☐   ☐

Add ☐

5. 141 - 73

How far from 100?   How far from 100?

☐   ☐

Add ☐

6. 125 - 84

How far from 100?   How far from 100?

☐   ☐

Add ☐

7. 129 - 80

How far from 100?   How far from 100?

☐   ☐

Add ☐

8. 124 - 88

How far from 100?   How far from 100?

☐   ☐

Add ☐

Subtracting, Using Amounts Above & Below 100

1. 106 - 97

How much above 100?　　How much below 100?

Add the two differences: ☐

2. 108 - 92

How much above 100?　　How much below 100?

Add the two differences: ☐

3. 110 - 89

How much above 100?　　How much below 100?

Add the two differences: ☐

4. 125 - 80

How much above 100?　　How much below 100?

Add the two differences: ☐

5. 112 - 60

How much above 100?　　How much below 100?

Add the two differences: ☐

6. 115 - 93

How much above 100?　　How much below 100?

Add the two differences: ☐

7. 120 - 88

How much above 100?　　How much below 100?

Add the two differences: ☐

8. 150 - 75

How much above 100?　　How much below 100?

Add the two differences: ☐

9. 180 - 85

How much above 100?　　How much below 100?

Add the two differences: ☐

10. 135 - 75

How much above 100?　　How much below 100?

Add the two differences: ☐

© Peter Wise, 2016

75

The DM-10 Trick

D – DIVIDE
M – MULTIPLY
10 – WITH TEN OR POWERS OF TEN
(100'S, 1000S, 10THS, 100THS, ETC.)

IF YOU MULTIPLY OR DIVIDE A NUMBER BY A POWER OF 10, YOU JUST SLIDE THE DECIMAL ON THE ORIGINAL NUMBER!

D (DIVIDE) ← When you divide by 10s you slide to the LEFT

M (MULTIPLY) → When you multiply by 10s you slide to the RIGHT

THIS IS WHY THE "D" COMES FIRST IN "DM-10"!

LET'S START BY DIVIDING BY 10S

WHEN YOU DIVIDE, YOU SLIDE TO THE LEFT!

Examples

A. $3.67 \div 10 =$ .367
←
ONE ZERO, ONE SLIDE!

B. $.42 \div 10 =$ .042

IF YOU NEED TO, ADD ONE OR MORE ZEROS TO GIVE ROOM TO SLIDE

(YOU CAN'T SLIDE IN BLANK SPACE!)

1. $37 \div 10 =$ ▢

REMEMBER! THERE IS AN INVISIBLE DECIMAL POINT HERE!

2. $9.2 \div 10 =$ ▢

3. $.8 \div 10 =$ ▢

4. $456 \div 10 =$ ▢

5. $800 \div 10 =$ ▢

6. $63.2 \div 10 =$ ▢

7. $800 \div 100 =$ ▢

TWO ZEROS, TWO SLIDES!

8. $751 \div 1,000 =$ ▢

STILL TO THE LEFT BECAUSE WE ARE DIVIDING!

HOW MANY SLIDES DO YOU THINK WITH THREE ZEROS?

9. $913.7 \div 1,000 =$ ▢

TIP: IT HELPS TO DRAW ARROWS FOR EACH SLIDE!

D (DIVIDE)   M (MULTIPLY)

←————————   ————————→

When you divide by 10s   When you multiply by 10s
you slide to the LEFT   you slide to the RIGHT

LET'S START BY
MULTIPLYING BY 10S

WHEN YOU MULTIPLY, YOU SLIDE TO THE RIGHT!

Examples

A. $4.23 \times 10 = \boxed{42.3}$

ONE ZERO, ONE SLIDE!

B. $12 \times 10 = \boxed{120}$

other ways of writing 12   12.
12.0

5. $80 \cdot 10 = \boxed{}$

6. $.09 \cdot 10 = \boxed{}$

7. $.09 \cdot 100 = \boxed{}$

8. $.0053 \cdot 100 = \boxed{}$

9. $.06 \cdot 1,000 = \boxed{}$

10. $4.38 \cdot 1,000 = \boxed{}$

11. $59.3 \cdot 100 = \boxed{}$

12. $364.2 \cdot 100 = \boxed{}$

1. $.62 \cdot 10 = \boxed{}$

2. $.357 \cdot 100 = \boxed{}$

3. $.78 \cdot 100 = \boxed{}$

4. $.7 \cdot 100 = \boxed{}$

The DM-10 Trick with Multiplication & Division

D (DIVIDE) ←——————→ **M** (MULTIPLY)

When you divide by 10s you slide to the LEFT

When you multiply by 10s you slide to the RIGHT

1. 350 · 10 = ☐

2. 350 ÷ 10 = ☐

3. 350 ÷ 100 = ☐

4. .79 · 10 = ☐

5. 4.26 · 10 = ☐

6. .06 · 100 = ☐

7. .75 · 100 = ☐

8. 6.3 · 10 = ☐

9. 6.3 · 100 = ☐

10. 2.7 · 1000 = ☐

11. .1 · 10 = ☐

12. .01 · 100 = ☐

13. 36 ÷ 10 = ☐

14. .004 · 100 = ☐

15. .004 · 1000 = ☐

16. 382 ÷ 100 = ☐

17. 7 ÷ 10 = ☐

18. 95 ÷ 1000 = ☐

19. 7.6 · 100 = ☐

20. .49 ÷ 10 = ☐

The DM-10 Trick with Multiplication & Division

D (DIVIDE) **M** (MULTIPLY)

←—————— ——————→

When you divide by 10s you slide to the LEFT

When you multiply by 10s you slide to the RIGHT

Count the zeros and slide!

1. $4 \cdot 100$ = ☐

2. $3 \div 10$ = ☐

3. $17 \div 100$ = ☐

4. $6 \div 100$ = ☐

5. $3.6 \cdot 10$ = ☐

6. $3.6 \cdot 100$ = ☐

7. $.07 \cdot 100$ = ☐

8. $.08 \cdot 1000$ = ☐

9. $45 \div 10$ = ☐

10. $6.03 \cdot 100$ = ☐

11. $27 \div 1000$ = ☐

12. $5 \div 1000$ = ☐

13. $.078 \cdot 1000$ = ☐

14. $.78 \cdot 1000$ = ☐

15. $4.6 \cdot 1000$ = ☐

16. $.27 \div 100$ = ☐

Review Problems

17. $3 + ☐ = 40$

18. $6 + ☐ = 80$

19. $12 + ☐ = 30$

20. $11 + ☐ = 50$

21. $14 + ☐ = 30$

22. $18 + ☐ = 100$

Powers of Ten

1. Skip count by 20s

20 ___ ___ ___ ___ ___ ___ ___ ___ ___ ___

2. Skip count by 30s

30 ___ ___ ___ ___ ___ ___ ___ ___ ___ ___

Examples

A.

10 as a factor 1 time

$$10^1 = 10$$

10

10 as a factor 2 times

$$10^2 = 100$$

1 and TWO zeros

$10 \cdot 10$

10 as a factor 3 times

$$10^3 = 1000$$

1 and THREE zeros

$10 \cdot 10 \cdot 10$

ANY NUMBER (EXCEPT 0) TO THE ZERO POWER = ONE!

B. $10^0 = 1$

NOT zero! $\cancel{0}$

1 and no zeros

---

1. $10^4 = $ ☐

2. $10^2 = $ ☐

3. $10^3 = $ ☐

4. $10^1 = $ ☐

5. $10^0 = $ ☐

6. $4 \cdot 10^2 = $ ☐

7. $.314 \cdot 10^2 = $ ☐

8. $.018 \cdot 10^4 = $ ☐

9. $.27 \cdot 10^3 = $ ☐

Write the correct exponents

10. $100 = 10^{\square}$

11. $10 = 10^{\square}$

12. $1000 = 10^{\square}$

13. $100,000 = 10^{\square}$

14. $10,000 = 10^{\square}$

15. $1 \text{ million} = 10^{\square}$

Multiply by powers of 10

16. $7 \cdot 10^2 = $ ☐

17. $72 \cdot 10^3 = $ ☐

18. $16 \cdot 10^0 = $ ☐

© Peter Wise, 2016

80

Multiplying by Multiples of Ten

When multiplying by 10, just add one zero onto the number, when multiplying by 100 add two zeros, when multiplying by 1000 add three zeros!

Example

1 zero 1 zero
A. $10 \cdot 3 = 30$

JUST ADD ONE ZERO ONTO THE THREE!

2 zeros 2 zeros
B. $100 \cdot 3 = 300$

Multiply by 10 or multiples of 10 (just add on the right number of zeros!)

1. $10 \cdot 6 =$

6. $10 \cdot 34 =$

11. $10 \cdot 75 =$

2. $10 \cdot 90 =$

7. $23 \cdot 100 =$

12. $60 \cdot 10 =$

3. $6 \cdot 10 =$

8. $4 \cdot 1000 =$

13. $100 \cdot 21 =$

4. $100 \cdot 7 =$

9. $16 \cdot 1000 =$

14. $28 \cdot 1000 =$

5. $10 \cdot 100 =$

10. $100 \cdot 5 =$

15. $10 \cdot 640 =$

Add or subtract mentally

16. $2560 + 233 =$

19. $5472 + 308 =$

17. $7350 + 2406 =$

20. $9765 - 314 =$

18. $4685 - 253 =$

21. $5000 - 265 =$

Multiplying by Multiples of Ten

Multiply the non-zero numbers first; then add on the number of zeros in the problem

1. 30 · 20 =

2. 40 · 600 =

3. 70 · 3 =

4. 30 · 90 =

5. 80 · 400 =

6. 20 · 1200 =

7. 500 · 700 =

8. 600 · 70 =

9. 90 · 500 =

10. 8 · 6000 =

11. 60 · 900 =

12. 110 · 300 =

13. 30 · 30 =

14. 800 · 800 =

15. 120 · 30 =

16. 70 · 40 =

17. 250 · 200 =

18. 70 · 900 =

19. 20 · 1700 =

20. 200 · 420 =

Division with Zeros

$$20 \overline{)40} = 2\overline{)4}^{\boxed{2}}$$

DIVIDING BOTH SIDES BY 10!

Same as the fraction $\dfrac{40}{20} = \dfrac{4}{2} = \boxed{2}$

Cancel the zeros from both sides and solve the following division problems

1. $200\overline{)400}$

HERE YOU CANCEL TWO ZEROS FROM BOTH SIDES!

Same as the fraction $\dfrac{400}{200}$

YOU CAN CANCEL THE SAME WAY WITH FRACTIONS!

2. $30\overline{)150}$

3. $600\overline{)1200}$

4. $600\overline{)120{,}000}$

5. $7000\overline{)420{,}000}$

6. $800\overline{)24{,}000}$

7. $50\overline{)250}$

8. $90\overline{)2700}$

9. $80\overline{)7200}$

10. $510\overline{)5100}$

11. $120\overline{)4800}$

12. $80\overline{)16{,}000}$

13. $4000\overline{)28{,}000}$

83

Mixed Review

Use the DM-10 Trick to multiply or divide the following numbers

1. 61 ÷ 10 = ☐

2. 7 ÷ 100 = ☐

3. 2.5 × 100 = ☐

4. 3.14 ÷ 100 = ☐

5. .017 ÷ 10 = ☐

6. .005 × 100 = ☐

Cancel the zeros from both sides and solve the following division problems

7. 40)2800

8. 800)3200

9. 7000)350,000

Double the following numbers by going LEFT to RIGHT

10. 37 + 37 =

will you have a carry?   y   n

add the TENS place
add 1 more for a carry → ☐ ☐

add the ONES place
LAST digit only

11. 29 + 29 =

will you have a carry?   y   n

add the TENS place
add 1 more for a carry → ☐ ☐

add the ONES place
LAST digit only

Cut the following numbers in half by breaking up the numbers into 10s and 1s

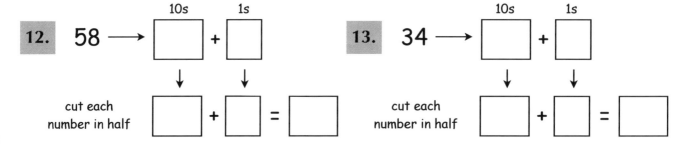

12. 58 →   10s ☐ + 1s ☐

cut each number in half   ☐ + ☐ = ☐

13. 34 →   10s ☐ + 1s ☐

cut each number in half   ☐ + ☐ = ☐

Mixed Review

Use the DM-10 Trick to multiply or divide the following numbers

1. $4.2 \times 10 \ = \ \boxed{}$

2. $3.14 \times 1000 = \boxed{}$

3. $.073 \times 1000 = \boxed{}$

4. $765 \div 100 = \boxed{}$

Add to the first number to round up, then subtract from the other number

5. $+\boxed{} \quad -\boxed{}$
$29 + 43 =$

New numbers: $\boxed{} + \boxed{} = \boxed{}$

6. $+\boxed{} \quad -\boxed{}$
$38 + 27 =$

New numbers: $\boxed{} + \boxed{} = \boxed{}$

7. $+\boxed{} \quad -\boxed{}$
$57 + 39 =$

New numbers: $\boxed{} + \boxed{} = \boxed{}$

8. $+\boxed{} \quad -\boxed{}$
$39 + 25 =$

New numbers: $\boxed{} + \boxed{} = \boxed{}$

Solve the following subtraction problems by subtracting in twice

9. $100 - 46$

$100 - \boxed{40} - \boxed{} = \boxed{}$

10. $100 - 37$

$100 - \boxed{} - \boxed{} = \boxed{}$

11. $70 - 24$

$70 - \boxed{} - \boxed{} = \boxed{}$

12. $54 - 26$

$54 - \boxed{} - \boxed{} = \boxed{}$

Calculate Mentally

1. 420 + 30 + 8 = ▢

2. 3600 + 200 + 7 = ▢

3. 670 + 19 = ▢

4. 5400 + 300 + 26 = ▢

5. 30 + 700 + 45

= ▢

6. 7900 + 400

= ▢

7. 680 + 25

= ▢

Calculating with Tens

8. 8 tens and 3 = ▢

9. 8 tens and 23 = ▢

10. .012 · 10 = ▢

11. 473 ÷ 100 = ▢

12. 7 + ▢ = 20

13. 12 + ▢ = 30

Division with Tens

14. 400)‾1200‾ with ▢

15. 60)‾5400‾ with ▢

16. 800)‾560000‾ with ▢

Put into "Standard Notation" (regular numbers)

17. 70 + 800 + 6 + .3 + .02 = ▢

© Peter Wise, 2016

86

The Triangle Trick

NUMBERS CAN BE WRITTEN AS SINGLE DIGITS FOLLOWED BY ZEROS. THE DIGITS AND ZEROS CAN BE MADE TO FORM A TRIANGLE.

This is called "Expanded Notation"

Make number triangles as in the example above

1. | 7 , 6 2 1 |

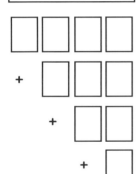

3. | 9 , 0 3 5 |

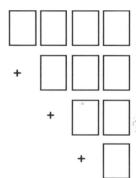

2. | 5 3 , 8 4 2 |

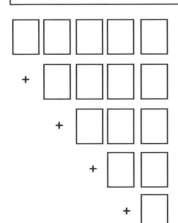

4. | 6 7 , 0 8 9 |

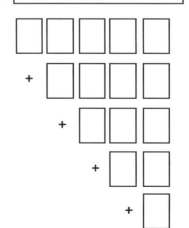

Expanded Notation With Powers of 10

YOU CAN EXPRESS EACH DIGIT OF A NUMBER AS A POWER OF 10!

6,735

$$6\ 0\ 0\ 0$$
$$+\quad 7\ 0\ 0$$
$$+\quad 3\ 0$$
$$+\quad 5$$

$6 \cdot 10^3$
$+\ 7 \cdot 10^2$
$+\ 3 \cdot 10^1$
$+\ 5 \cdot 10^0$

THE EXPONENT ON THE 10 IS THE SAME AS THE NUMBER OF ZEROS!

ANY NUMBER TO THE ZERO POWER = 1!

---EXCEPT ZERO!

THIS IS ANOTHER WAY TO WRITE EXPANDED NOTATION!

Make number triangles as in the example above

TIMES 10^3 10^2 10^1 10^0

1.   7 , 6   2   8

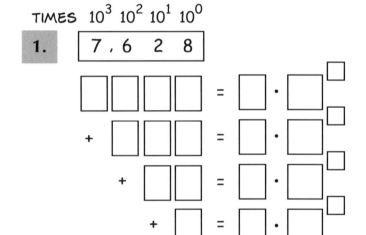

3.   5 , 3   1   4

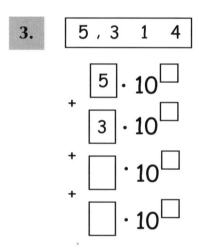

2.   4   9 , 2   3   7

4.   8   7 , 4   6   2

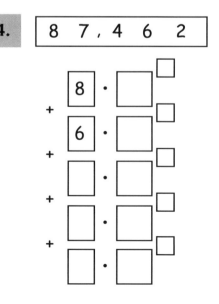

Mixed Review

Fill in the number triangles

1. | 5 , 2 | 8 | 3 |

$$
\begin{array}{c}
\square\square\square\square \\
+ \quad \square\square\square \\
+ \quad \square\square \\
+ \quad \square
\end{array}
$$

3. | 8 , 0 | 9 | 7 |

$$
\begin{array}{c}
\square\square\square\square \\
+ \quad \square\square\square \\
+ \quad \square\square \\
+ \quad \square
\end{array}
$$

Fill in the number triangle using powers of 10

2. | 2 | 3 , 1 | 6 | 4 |

$$
\begin{array}{ccccc}
\square\square\square\square\square & = & \square & \cdot & \square^{\square} \\
+ \quad \square\square\square\square & = & \square & \cdot & \square^{\square} \\
+ \quad \square\square\square & = & \square & \cdot & \square^{\square} \\
+ \quad \square\square & = & \square & \cdot & \square^{\square} \\
+ \quad \square & = & \square & \cdot & \square^{\square}
\end{array}
$$

Add the following numbers mentally; line them up correctly in your head!

3. $250 + 20 + 6 =$ [ ]

5. $640 + 30 + 15 =$ [ ]

4. $9 + 320 + 30 =$ [ ]

6. $270 + 40 + 16 =$ [ ]

Intro to Rounding

Example

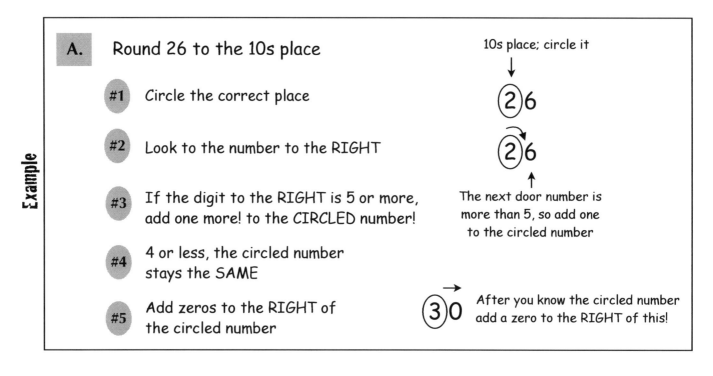

A. Round 26 to the 10s place

- **#1** Circle the correct place
- **#2** Look to the number to the RIGHT
- **#3** If the digit to the RIGHT is 5 or more, add one more! to the CIRCLED number!
- **#4** 4 or less, the circled number stays the SAME
- **#5** Add zeros to the RIGHT of the circled number

10s place; circle it

②6

②6

The next door number is more than 5, so add one to the circled number

③0

After you know the circled number add a zero to the RIGHT of this!

Round the following numbers to the 10s place

Remember to circle the 10s place digit & draw an arrow to the right

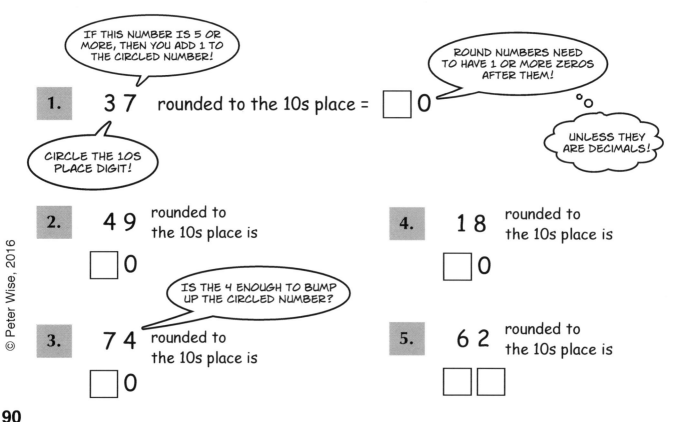

IF THIS NUMBER IS 5 OR MORE, THEN YOU ADD 1 TO THE CIRCLED NUMBER!

ROUND NUMBERS NEED TO HAVE 1 OR MORE ZEROS AFTER THEM!

1. 3 7   rounded to the 10s place = ☐ 0

UNLESS THEY ARE DECIMALS!

CIRCLE THE 10S PLACE DIGIT!

2. 4 9   rounded to the 10s place is
☐ 0

4. 1 8   rounded to the 10s place is
☐ 0

IS THE 4 ENOUGH TO BUMP UP THE CIRCLED NUMBER?

3. 7 4   rounded to the 10s place is
☐ 0

5. 6 2   rounded to the 10s place is
☐ ☐

Rounding to the 10's Place

Round the following numbers to the 10s place

Circle the 10s place digit and draw an arrow to the right

1. 3 6   rounded to the 10s place is

☐ 0

2. 2 5

☐ 0

3. 9 8

☐ ☐ 0

4. 6 4

☐ ☐

5. 6 5

☐ ☐

6. 8 6

☐ ☐

7. 1 3

☐ ☐

8. 5 5

☐ ☐

9. 2 7

☐ ☐

10. 9 2

☐ ☐

11. 8 8

☐ ☐

12. 1 5

☐ ☐

Rounding to the 10's Place: 3-Digit Numbers

A. Round 6 3 9 to the 10s place

↑

#1 Round the 10s place digit normally

#2 COPY the digit to the LEFT of the circle number

#3 Put a ZERO to the RIGHT of the circle number

HOW TO FIND THE 10'S PLACE:

6 3 9   5 2 3 3
↑   ↑
1 0s   1 0s

Write or imagine a 10 lined up on the RIGHT side

The 1 on the ten points up to the 10s place!

Example

6 ③ 9   rounded to the 10s place is

COPY the numbers ←   → Zeros on this side
on this side

6 ④ 0

Round the following numbers to the 10s place

Circle the 10s place digit and draw an arrow to the right

1. 7 5 8   rounded to the 10s place is

7 ☐ 0

2. 2 1 6   rounded to the 10s place is

☐ ☐ 0

3. 4 7 4   rounded to the 10s place is

☐ ☐ ☐

4. 1 4 5

☐ ☐ ☐

5. 4 4 4

☐ ☐ ☐

6. 5 5 5

☐ ☐ ☐

7. 2 7 6

☐ ☐ ☐

8. 3 0 5

☐ ☐ ☐

9. 9 1 4

☐ ☐ ☐

Rounding with Carrying

You will only carry if the circle number is 9

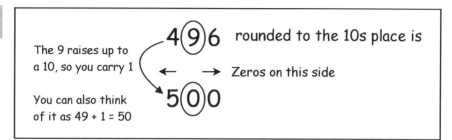

A.

Example

The 9 raises up to a 10, so you carry 1

You can also think of it as 49 + 1 = 50

4(9)6 rounded to the 10s place is

← → Zeros on this side

5(0)0

Round the following numbers to the 10s place (not all problems have a carry)

Remember to circle the 10s place digit and draw an arrow to the right

1. 2 9 8 rounded to the 10s place is

☐ ☐ 0

WHAT HAPPENS IF YOU ADD 1 TO 9?

2. 8 9 7 rounded to the 10s place is

☐ ☐ 0

3. 1 9 4

☐ ☐ ☐

4. 5 9 5

☐ ☐ ☐

5. 8 0 5

☐ ☐ ☐

6. 8 0 4

☐ ☐ ☐

7. 3 4 4

☐ ☐ ☐

8. 5 9 6

☐ ☐ ☐

9. 9 5

☐ ☐ ☐

10. 7 8 9

☐ ☐ ☐

11. 7 9 8

☐ ☐ ☐

12. 4 1 3

☐ ☐ ☐

13. 7 2 7

☐ ☐ ☐

14. 9 9 5

☐ ☐ ☐ ☐

Rounding 4-Digit Numbers

A. **If you round to the 10s place**

2 3 ⑦ 6 rounded to the 10s place:

COPY on this side ←   → ZEROS on this side

2 3 ⑧ 0

B. **If you round to the 100s place**

2 ③ 7 6 rounded to the 100s place:

COPY on this side ←   → ZEROS on this side

2 ④ 0 0

Round the following numbers to the proper place

Remember to circle the digit in the correct place

1. 1 2 8 6 rounded to the 10s place is
☐ ☐ ☐ ☐

2. 1 2 8 6 rounded to the 100s place is
☐ ☐ ☐ ☐

3. 5 8 7 3 rounded to the 10s place is
☐ ☐ ☐ ☐

4. 5 8 7 3 rounded to the 100s place is
☐ ☐ ☐ ☐

5. 4 1 9 6 rounded to the 10s place is
☐ ☐ ☐ ☐

6. 3 0 0 7 rounded to the 10s place is
☐ ☐ ☐ ☐

7. 3 0 0 7 rounded to the 100s place is
☐ ☐ ☐ ☐

8. 2 9 7 1 rounded to the 100s place is
☐ ☐ ☐ ☐

9. 6 1 9 8 rounded to the 10s place is
☐ ☐ ☐ ☐

10. 2 3 7 5 rounded to the 10s place is
☐ ☐ ☐ ☐

94

Rounding to the Ones Place

Look next door

A. Round 3⑦.8 2 to the 1s place = |3 8|

or 3 8 . 0 0

↑
You don't need
these decimals

- **#1** Circle the ONEs place
- **#2** If the digit next door is 5 or more add 1 to the circled number
- **#3** COPY the digits to the LEFT of the circle number
- **#4** You don't need any decimals numbers or even the decimal point if you're rounding to the ones place!

Round the following numbers to the ones place

Don't forget the circles & arrows

1. 8 . 6   rounded to the 1s place is

☐

2. 2 . 6 7

☐

3. 4 5 . 3

☐

4. 7 8 . 5 1

☐

5. 4 3 5 . 7 9

☐

6. 6 1 . 8 2 7

☐

7. 2 9 0 . 6 0 2

☐

8. 1 5 . 0 9

☐

95

Rounding to the Tenths Place

A. Round 2 3 . ①6 to the 10ths place = 2 3 . 2

#1 Round the 10s place digit normally

#2 COPY the digit to the LEFT of the circle number

#3 Put a ZERO to the RIGHT of the circle number

#4 You can ignore the zeros to the right of the rounded tenths place

HOW TO FIND THE TENTHS PLACE:

2 3 . 1 6

10ths

With decimals numbers, the 1 points to the decimal and you have a zero for every decimal

10 has one zero
There is one zero for each decimal place

Round the following numbers to the tenths place; remember the circles & arrows

1. 3 . 6 5

5. 1 0 . 1 2

9. 1 8 . 6 7 2

2. 1 5 . 8 6

6. 2 4 . 0 4

10. 6 . 0 0 9

3. 9 . 1 7 2

7. 3 7 . 5 5

11. 8 2 . 5 0 8

4. 5 6 . 0 9

8. 9 0 5 . 4 6

12. 2 . 4 9 9

Mixed Review

Round the following numbers to the 10s place

1. 7 5
↓
☐ 0

2. 2 6
↓
☐ 0

3. 5 4
☐ ☐

4. 3 9
☐ ☐

5. 4 3
☐ ☐

6. 6 6
☐ ☐

Round the following 3-digit numbers to the TENS place

7. 3 7 2   rounded to the TENS place is
↓
3 ☐ 0

8. 4 2 8   rounded to the 10s place is
☐ ☐ 0

9. 3 0 7
☐ ☐ ☐

10. 5 8 2
☐ ☐ ☐

11. 2 5 5
☐ ☐ ☐

12. 6 2 5
☐ ☐ ☐

Find the sum

12. 9 tens and 37 = ☐

13. 16 tens and 26 = ☐

Add the original numbers, add the additional tens, solve the new problems

14. 9 + 8 = ☐   29 + 28

how much more is this? ☐

29 + 28 = ☐

15. 17 + 6 = ☐   47 + 26

how much more is this? ☐

47 + 26 = ☐

97

Mixed Review

Calculate the tens and the ones; then add them together

1. 4 tens and 17 = ☐   **3.** 14 tens and 25 = ☐

2. 8 tens and 23 = ☐   **4.** 15 tens and 42 = ☐

Double the following numbers

5. 23 → ☐   **7.** 37 → ☐   **9.** 239 → ☐

6. 19 → ☐   **8.** 48 → ☐   **10.** 366 → ☐

Cut the following numbers in half by breaking up the numbers into 10s and 1s

11. 78 ⟶ ☐ + ☐   **12.** 34 ⟶ ☐ + ☐

cut each number in half   ☐ + ☐ = ☐   ☐ + ☐ = ☐

Round the following numbers to the ONES place

13. 5 . 4   rounded to the 1s place is   ☐

14. 7 2 . 6 4   ☐

15. 3 1 5 . 4 5   ☐

Round the following numbers to the TENTHS place

16. 6 . 3 5   ☐

17. 3 . 5 4   ☐

18. 1 3 . 7 5 4   ☐

What Does the Mean Mean?

Example

A. Find the mean of 3 and 7:

$(3 + 7) \div 2 = \boxed{10}$ or $\dfrac{(3 + 7)}{2} = \boxed{10}$

> DIVIDE BY 2 BECAUSE YOU ADDED 2 NUMBERS!

Add the numbers and divide by the # of numbers you added!

Find the mean (average) of the following numbers

1. 2 and 6

$(\boxed{} + \boxed{}) \div \boxed{} = \boxed{}$

add first   then divide

2. 5 and 7

$(\boxed{} + \boxed{}) \div \boxed{} = \boxed{}$

add first   then divide

3. 2 and 10

$(\boxed{} + \boxed{}) \div \boxed{} = \boxed{}$

add first   then divide

4. 3 and 15

$(\boxed{}) \div \boxed{} = \boxed{}$

5. 4 and 20

$(\boxed{}) \div \boxed{} = \boxed{}$

6. 5 and 9

$(\boxed{}) \div \boxed{} = \boxed{}$

7. 8 and 8

$(\boxed{}) \div \boxed{} = \boxed{}$

8. 13 and 7

$(\boxed{}) \div \boxed{} = \boxed{}$

> 13 IS 3 ABOVE THIS
> 7 IS 3 BELOW THIS!

9. 25 and 5

$(\boxed{}) \div \boxed{} = \boxed{}$

10. 10 and 32

$(\boxed{}) \div \boxed{} = \boxed{}$

What Does the Mean Mean?

The Mean (aka "average") is the middle between two numbers; "equal piles"

Draw a point for each of the numbers and for the mean

You find the mean by adding the numbers and dividing by the number of addends

1. 3 and 5

([   ]) ÷ [   ] = [   ]

add 3 + 5   then divide by 2 (because you added two numbers)

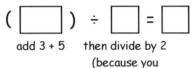

PUT A DOT ON 3, 5, AND THE MEAN! ...WHAT DO YOU NOTICE?

2. 2 and 8

([   ]) ÷ [   ] = [   ]

3. 1 and 11

([   ]) ÷ [   ] = [   ]

4. 10 and 14

([   ]) ÷ [   ] = [   ]

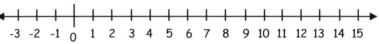

THE MEAN (AVERAGE) LEVELS ALL OF THE NUMBERS

5. 4 + 6 = [   ] What is the mean of 4 and 6? ([   ]) ÷ [   ] = [   ]

[   ] + [   ] = [   ] (same as 4 + 6)

mean + mean

6. 3 + 11 = [   ] What is the mean of 3 and 11? ([   ]) ÷ [   ] = [   ]

[   ] + [   ] = [   ] (same as 3 + 11)

mean + mean

Mean Practice

Find the mean (average) of the following numbers

1. 3, 7, and 8 ← 3 numbers

(☐ + ☐ + ☐) ÷ ☐ = ☐

add first   then divide

ADD THE MULTIPLES OF 5 FIRST!

8. 2, 15, 10, 5, and 3

☐ ÷ ☐ = ☐

2. 10, 6, and 8

(☐ + ☐ + ☐) ÷ ☐ = ☐

add first   then divide

9. 9, 7, 1, and 3

☐ ÷ ☐ = ☐

3. 40, 20, 30

☐ ÷ ☐ = ☐

10. 15, 10, 5, 18

☐ ÷ ☐ = ☐

4. 2, 5, and 8

☐ ÷ ☐ = ☐

11. 10, 12, 8, and 2

☐ ÷ ☐ = ☐

REMEMBER TO DIVIDE BY THE NUMBER OF ADDENDS IN THE PROBLEM!

5. 10, 10, 2, and 6

☐ ÷ ☐ = ☐

12. 50, 10, 5, and 15

☐ ÷ ☐ = ☐

6. 4, 2 and 6

☐ ÷ ☐ = ☐

13. 2, 3, 10, 3, and 7

☐ ÷ ☐ = ☐

7. 4, 20, and 6

☐ ÷ ☐ = ☐

14. 12, 6, 1, 2, and 9

☐ ÷ ☐ = ☐

101

Mean Practice

1. 2, 4, 2, 4

(☐) ÷ ☐ = ☐

2. 6, 12, 3

☐ ÷ ☐ = ☐

3. 13, 9, 2

☐ ÷ ☐ = ☐

4. 8, 3, 12, 1

☐ ÷ ☐ = ☐

5. 3, 11, 6, 3, 2

☐ ÷ ☐ = ☐

6. 6, 20, 8, 10

☐ ÷ ☐ = ☐

7. 20, 15, 25, 30, 10

☐ ÷ ☐ = ☐

8. 5, 5, 25, 5

☐ ÷ ☐ = ☐

9. 70, 70, 10

☐ ÷ ☐ = ☐

10. 5, 10, 30

☐ ÷ ☐ = ☐

11. 20, 40, 15

☐ ÷ ☐ = ☐

12. 5, 10, 15, 30

☐ ÷ ☐ = ☐

13. 7, 8, 8, 7, 5

WHICH 2 PAIRS OF NUMBERS WOULD BE BEST TO ADD FIRST?

☐ ÷ ☐ = ☐

14. 24, 15, 30, 11

☐ ÷ ☐ = ☐

Mean Practice

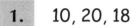

Find the mean (average) of the following numbers

1. 10, 20, 18

☐ ÷ ☐ = ☐

2. 24, 40

☐ ÷ ☐ = ☐

3. 3, 11, 7

☐ ÷ ☐ = ☐

4. 10, 10, 19

☐ ÷ ☐ = ☐

5. 16, 18

☐ ÷ ☐ = ☐

6. 30, 50, 20, 20

☐ ÷ ☐ = ☐

7. 50, 70, 60

☐ ÷ ☐ = ☐

8. 13, 17, 10, 12, 18

☐ ÷ ☐ = ☐

9. 10, 14, 6, 8, 8, 8

☐ ÷ ☐ = ☐

10. 18, 12, 6

☐ ÷ ☐ = ☐

11. 6, 12, 7, 7

☐ ÷ ☐ = ☐

12. 30, 24

☐ ÷ ☐ = ☐

13. 100, 50, 60

☐ ÷ ☐ = ☐

14. 50, 25, 25, 200, 150

☐ ÷ ☐ = ☐

Intro to the Median

How do you find the Median?

Example

A.   12, 8, 3, 13, 7

#1   Line the numbers up in order: 3, 7, 8, 12, 13
↑

#2   Find the middle number; this is the MEDIAN

#3   With longer strings of numbers it can help to cross off the smallest number, greatest number, next smallest, etc. When you get to the middle, you have found the MEDIAN

4, 4, 5, 8, 10, 10, 13, 14, 18, 18, 19, 25, 30
↓

#4   What if there are two middle numbers? Then you find the MEAN of the two middle numbers. This will be the MEDIAN!   3, 8, 10, 18
↑

Use the MEAN of the two MIDDLE NUMBERS

YOU CAN TELL THAT THE NUMBER BETWEEN 8 AND 10 IS 9 (THE MEAN)!

Find the MEDIAN of the following numbers

1.   10, 9, 5, 4, 14

☐   Median = ☐
put them in order

2.   7, 11, 2 , 7, 10

TREAT DOUBLE NUMBERS JUST LIKE REGULAR NUMBERS!

☐   Median = ☐
put them in order

3.   3, 2, 11, 6, 10, 4   Median = ☐

☐

4.   9, 15, 8, 3, 25, 14, 21   Median = ☐

☐

5.   20, 10, 5, 6, 12, 5   Median = ☐

☐

6.   12, 19, 5, 15, 2, 6   Median = ☐

☐

104

Mean, Median, Mode

Find the MEAN, MEDIAN, and MODE of the following numbers

Mode = number that occurs the most

Median = middle number

Mean = add the numbers, divide by the number of addends

© Peter Wise, 2016

1. 1, 3, 26

Mean: ☐

2. 2, 7, 8

Median: ☐

3. 14, 5, 8, 14

Mode: ☐

> THE *MODE* IS THE NUMBER THAT OCCURS THE *MOST*!

> THIS NUMBER OCCURS THE *"MODST"* OFTEN!

4. 4, 4, 12, 30, 50

Median: ☐

5. 30, 50, 10

Mean: ☐

6. 7, 25, 6, 6

Mode: ☐

7. 2, 8, 10, 12

Median: ☐

8. 1, 8, 9

Mean: ☐

9. 2, 6, 29, 6, 30

Mode: ☐

10. 3, 5, 7

Median ☐

11. 3, 12, 14, 18

Median ☐

12. 1, 3, 5, 15

Median: ☐

13. 4, 4, 10, 2, 5

Mean: ☐

14. 3, 4, 11

Mean: ☐

15. 3, 7, 9, 10

Median: ☐

16. 20, 40, 60

Mean: ☐

17. 2, 11, 13, 16

Median: ☐

105

Mean, Median, Mode

Find the MEAN, MEDIAN, and MODE of the following numbers

Mode = number that occurs the most

Median = middle number

Mean = add the numbers, divide by the number of addends

1. 2, 3, 5, 9

Median: ☐

2. 5, 16, 16, 18

Mode: ☐

3. 3, 6, 12

Mean: ☐

4. 2, 6, 12, 13, 14

Median: ☐

5. 2, 8, 14, 14

Mode: ☐

6. 24, 27, 31

Median: ☐

7. 3, 8, 11, 14, 16

Median: ☐

8. 14, 3, 15, 16, 14

Mode: ☐

9. 3, 17, 4

Mean: ☐

10. 14, 15, 17, 19

Median ☐

11. 1, 20, 6

Mean: ☐

12. 8, 2, 5, 8, 7

Mode: ☐

13. 3, 16, 18, 20

Median: ☐

14. 2, 11, 2

Mean: ☐

15 9, 12, 21, 9, 25

Mode: ☐

16 15, 10, 5

Mean: ☐

17 4, 7, 9, 10

Median: ☐

106

Mean, Median, Mode

Find the MEAN, MEDIAN, and MODE of the following numbers

1. 18, 6, 3

Mean: ☐

2. 14, 1, 3

Median ☐

3. 3, 5, 6, 10, 16

Median: ☐

4. 2, 5, 7, 12, 18

Median: ☐

5. 4, 18, 2

Mean: ☐

6. 3, 5, 3, 8, 11

Mode: ☐

7. 2, 4, 6, 7

Median: ☐

8. 14, 27, 14, 39

Mode: ☐

9. 2, 18, 7

Mean: ☐

10. 3, 7, 3, 9

Mode: ☐

11. 1, 5, 7, 12

Median ☐

12. 14, 20, 2

Mean: ☐

13. 4, 7, 8

Median ☐

14. 4, 5, 5, 9

Mode ☐

15. 20, 8, 5

Mean: ☐

16. 30, 80, 80, 20

Mode ☐

107

Multiplying by Fives

Explanation

5 is half of 10

When you multiply by 5 it's the same as

OR

$(\times 10)$ and $(\div 2)$

$(\div 2)$ and $(\times 10)$

↑ Cut the number in half (divide by 2)

↑ Multiply by 10 (add on a zero)

Example

Cut in half; add a zero trick

12×5

Divide by 2 → 6

Add on a zero   6 0
↑

Multiply by 5 by dividing by 2 and then adding a zero at the end

---

1. $8 \times 5 =$

Half of 8 $(8 \div 2)$ ☐ ☐ Add on a zero

2. $6 \times 5 =$

Half of 6 (divide by 2)   ☐ ☐ Add on a zero

3. $14 \times 5 =$

Half of 14   ☐ ☐ Add on a zero

4. $18 \times 5 =$

Divide by 2   ☐ ☐ Add on a zero

5. $24 \times 5 =$

Divide by 2   ☐ ☐ Add on a zero

6. $28 \times 5 =$

☐ ☐ Add on a zero

7. $60 \times 5 =$

☐ Add on a zero

8. $32 \times 5 =$

☐

9. $44 \times 5 =$

☐ Add on a zero

10. $48 \times 5 =$

☐ Add on a zero

Multiplying by Fives

Multiply by 5 by dividing by 2 and then adding a zero at the end

1. 34 × 5 =

Half of 34 [ ] [ ] Add on a zero

2. 38 × 5 =

Half of 38 [ ] [ ] Add on a zero

3. 42 × 5 =

[ ] Add on a zero

4. 64 × 5 =

[ ]

5. 36 × 5 =

[ ]

6. 52 × 5 =

[ ]

7. 54 × 5 =

[ ]

8. 58 × 5 =

[ ]

9. 66 × 5 =

[ ]

10. 26 × 5 =

[ ]

11. 78 × 5 =

[ ]

12. 86 × 5 =

[ ]

13. 76 × 5 =

[ ]

14. 98 × 5 =

[ ]

Multiplying by Fives

Multiply by 5 by dividing by 2 and then adding a zero at the end

1. 5 × 2 6 8 =

Half of 2   Half of 6   Half of 8   Add on a zero

2. 5 × 6 4 2 =

Half of 6   Half of 4   Half of 2   Add on a zero

3. 5 × 8 0 4 6 =

half of   8   0   4   6

4. 5 × 1 0 6 4 =

half of 10   64   Add on a zero

5. 5 × 3 6 3 8 =

half of   36   38

6. 5 × 3 4 1 6 =

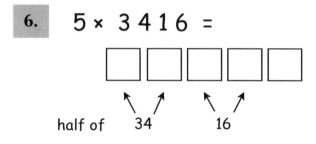

half of   34   16

7. 5 × 5 2 1 4 =

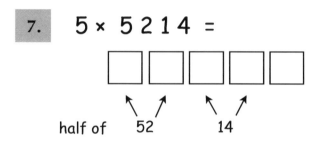

half of   52   14

8. 5 × 8 6 5 4 =

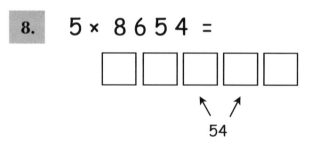

54

9. 5 × 5 0 6 8 =

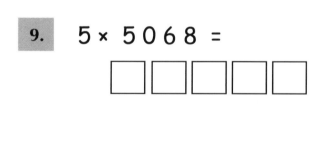

10. 5 × 7 0 5 6 =

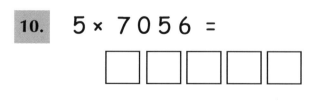

Multiplying by Fives

Multiply by 5 by dividing by 2 and then sliding the decimal point one time to the RIGHT

Sliding the decimal point one time to the right is the same as multiplying by 10

1.   4 8 . 2 6 × 5 =

slide the decimal one time to the RIGHT (same as multiplying by 10)

half of   4   8   2   6

2.   6 . 2 4 8 × 5 =

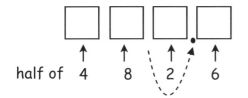

...BECAUSE THE WAY WE'RE MULTIPLYING BY 5 IS "DIVIDE BY 2; TIMES 10!"

3.   8 0 . 5 4 × 5 =

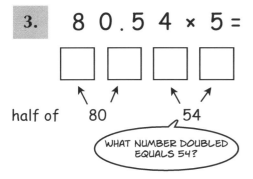

half of   80   54

WHAT NUMBER DOUBLED EQUALS 54?

4.   2 6 . 5 2 × 5 =

half of   26   52

5.   3 . 6 8 4 × 5 =

6.   3 . 8 0 6 × 5 =

7.   3 0 3 . 2 × 5 =

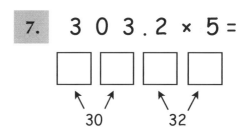

30   32

8.   5 . 2 1 8 × 5 =

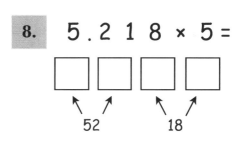

52   18

9.   . 5 6 2 4 × 5 =

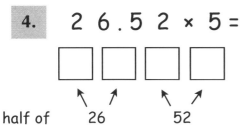

56

10.   7 2 . 5 8 × 5 =

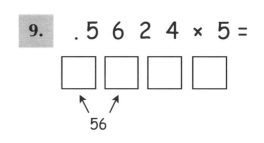

Multiplying Odd Numbers by 5's

Any ODD number times 5 ends in FIVE

$7 \times 5 =$

#1 Subtract 1 from the 7 → 6 $(7 - 1 = 6)$

#2 Divide by 2, but now add on a 5 → 3 5

Multiply by 5 by dividing by 2 and then adding on a five at the end

1. 3×5

Subtract 1 from the 3 ☐

Divide by 2, add on a 5 ☐

4. 15×5

Subtract 1 from the 15 ☐

Divide by 2, add on a 5 ☐

7. 43×5

Subtract 1 from the 43 ☐

Divide by 2, add on a 5 ☐

2. 9×5

Subtract 1 from the 9 ☐

Divide by 2, add on a 5 ☐

5. 31×5

Subtract 1 from the 31 ☐

Divide by 2, add on a 5 ☐

8. 87×5

Subtract 1 from the 87 ☐

Divide by 2, add on a 5 ☐

3. 13×5

Subtract 1 from the 13 ☐

Divide by 2, add on a 5 ☐

6. 37×5

Subtract 1 from the 37 ☐

Divide by 2, add on a 5 ☐

9. 59×5

Subtract 1 from the 59 ☐

Divide by 2, add on a 5 ☐

Multiplying Odd Numbers by 5's

Multiply by 5 by dividing by 2, adding a zero, and then adding 5

1. 17×5

Subtract 1 from the 17 ☐

Divide by 2, add on a 5 ☐

5. 23×5

Subtract 1 from the 23 ☐

Divide by 2, add on a 5 ☐

9. 33×5

Subtract 1 from the 33 ☐

Divide by 2, add on a 5 ☐

2. 43×5

Subtract 1 ☐

Divide by 2, add on a 5 ☐

6. 19×5

Subtract 1 ☐

Divide by 2, add on a 5 ☐

10. 27×5

Subtract 1 ☐

Divide by 2, add on a 5 ☐

3. 37×5

Subtract 1 ☐

Divide by 2, add on a 5 ☐

7. 53×5

Subtract 1 ☐

Divide by 2, add on a 5 ☐

11. 65×5

Subtract 1 ☐

Divide by 2, add on a 5 ☐

4. 21×5

Subtract 1 ☐

Divide by 2, add on a 5 ☐

8. 67×5

Subtract 1 ☐

Divide by 2, add on a 5 ☐

12. 77×5

Subtract 1 ☐

Divide by 2, add on a 5 ☐

113

Multiplying When Adding

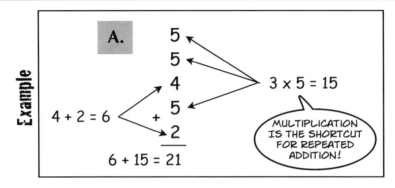

Example

A.

$$5$$
$$5$$
$$4$$
$$5$$
$$+ \quad 2$$

$4 + 2 = 6$

$3 \times 5 = 15$

$6 + 15 = 21$

MULTIPLICATION IS THE SHORTCUT FOR REPEATED ADDITION!

When you add the same number more than once, think MULTIPLY!

Multiply the repeated numbers and add to find the total

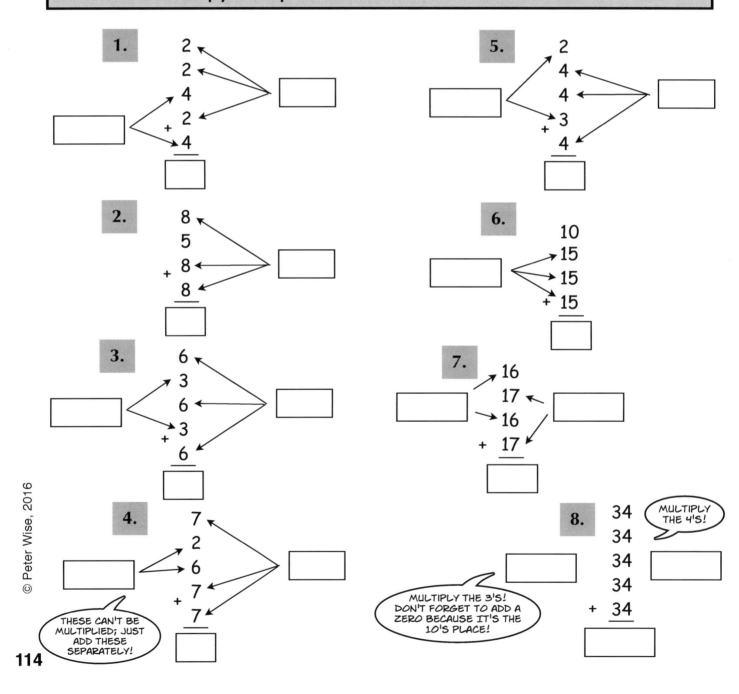

1.

$$2$$
$$2$$
$$4$$
$$2$$
$$+ \quad 4$$

2.

$$8$$
$$5$$
$$+ \quad 8$$
$$8$$

3.

$$6$$
$$3$$
$$6$$
$$3$$
$$+ \quad 6$$

4.

$$7$$
$$2$$
$$6$$
$$7$$
$$+ \quad 7$$

THESE CAN'T BE MULTIPLIED; JUST ADD THESE SEPARATELY!

5.

$$2$$
$$4$$
$$4$$
$$3$$
$$+ \quad 4$$

6.

$$10$$
$$15$$
$$15$$
$$+ \quad 15$$

7.

$$16$$
$$17$$
$$16$$
$$+ \quad 17$$

8.

$$34$$
$$34$$
$$34$$
$$34$$
$$+ \quad 34$$

MULTIPLY THE 4'S!

MULTIPLY THE 3'S! DON'T FORGET TO ADD A ZERO BECAUSE IT'S THE 10'S PLACE!

Sum and Product

Find the SUM and the PRODUCT of the following numbers

SUM = answer to an ADDITION problem; PRODUCT = answer to a MULTIPLICATION problem

			sum	product
1.	7	3		
2.	5	4		
3.	6	2		
4.	3	8		
5.	9	3		
6.	3	4		
7.	8	7		
8.	2	9		
9.	6	4		
10.	7	5		
11.	8	6		
12.	4	9		

			sum	product
13.	5	8		
14.	2	12		
15.	3	11		
16.	3	12		
17.	8	8		
18.	9	7		
19.	6	9		
20.	5	12		
21.	8	9		
22.	12	4		
23.	7	12		
24.	25	3		

115

Difference and Quotient

Find the DIFFERENCE and the QUOTIENT of the following numbers

DIFFERENCE = answer to a SUBTRACTION problem; QUOTIENT = answer to a DIVISION problem

			difference	quotient					difference	quotient
1.	8	2				13.	25	5		
2.	15	5				14.	28	4		
3.	12	3				15.	12	4		
4.	16	2				16.	35	7		
5.	18	3				17.	32	8		
6.	20	5				18.	48	8		
7.	70	10				19.	24	8		
8.	24	6				20.	54	6		
9.	14	2				21.	64	8		
10.	16	4				22.	63	9		
11.	24	2				23.	56	8		
12.	30	6				24.	84	7		

4 Operations with Numbers

			sum	product	difference	quotient
A.	6	2	8	12	4	3

Perform all four operations with the given numbers

			sum	product	difference	quotient
1.	10	2				
2.	10	5				
3.	9	3				
4.	5	1				
5.	12	3				
6.	8	4				
7.	15	3				
8.	12	4				
9.	20	2				
10.	50	2				

117

4 Operations with Numbers

		sum	product	difference	quotient
1.	20 5				
2.	60 2				
3.	100 10				
4.	20 4				
5.	50 10				
6.	30 2				
7.	100 4				
8.	40 20				
9.	6 3				
10.	24 2				
11.	80 40				
12.	16 2				

© Peter Wise, 2016

118

Finding New Factor Pairs

Use just these factors to make different multiplication problems

1. $3 \cdot 4 = \boxed{}$

$\cdot 2 \quad \div 2$

$\boxed{} \cdot \boxed{} = \boxed{}$

2. $4 \cdot 4 = \boxed{}$

$\div 2 \quad \cdot 2$

$\boxed{} \cdot \boxed{} = \boxed{}$

3. $2 \cdot 9 = \boxed{}$

$\cdot 3 \quad \div 3$

$\boxed{} \cdot \boxed{} = \boxed{}$

4. $6 \cdot 8 = \boxed{}$

$\cdot 2 \quad \div 2$

$\boxed{} \cdot \boxed{} = \boxed{}$

5. $4 \cdot 5 = \boxed{}$

$\div 2 \quad \cdot 2$

$\boxed{} \cdot \boxed{} = \boxed{}$

6. $6 \cdot 5 = \boxed{}$

$\div 2 \quad \cdot 2$

$\boxed{} \cdot \boxed{} = \boxed{}$

7. $4 \cdot 6 = \boxed{}$

$\cdot 2 \quad \div 2$

$\boxed{} \cdot \boxed{} = \boxed{}$

8. $6 \cdot 6 = \boxed{}$

$\div 2 \quad \cdot 2$

$\boxed{} \cdot \boxed{} = \boxed{}$

9. $5 \cdot 8 = \boxed{}$

$\cdot 2 \quad \div 2$

$\boxed{} \cdot \boxed{} = \boxed{}$

10. $10 \cdot 6 = \boxed{}$

$\div 2 \quad \cdot 2$

$\boxed{} \cdot \boxed{} = \boxed{}$

119

Multiply/Divide by the Same Amount

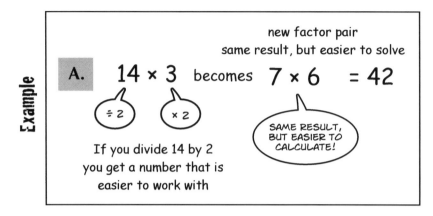

Example

A. 14 × 3 becomes 7 × 6 = 42

new factor pair
same result, but easier to solve

÷ 2   × 2

If you divide 14 by 2
you get a number that is
easier to work with

SAME RESULT,
BUT EASIER TO
CALCULATE!

Rewrite these multiplication problems by multiplying & dividing by the same amounts

Your factor pairs should be normal times table numbers

1. 16 × 4

÷ ☐ × ☐

☐ • ☐ = ☐

new factor pair

2. 18 × 2

÷ ☐ × ☐

THERE ARE TWO
DIFFERENT PAIRS
THAT WORK FOR THIS
PROBLEM!

☐ • ☐ = ☐

new factor pair

3. 24 × 6

÷ ☐ × ☐

SOMETIMES YOU HAVE TO
TRY DIFFERENT
COMBINATIONS UNTIL YOU
GET A PAIR THAT IS EASY
TO WORK WITH

☐ • ☐ = ☐

new factor pair

4. 28 × 3

÷ ☐ × ☐

☐ • ☐ = ☐

new factor pair

5 16 × 5

÷ ☐ × ☐

☐ • ☐ = ☐

new factor pair

6. 32 × 3

÷ ☐ × ☐

☐ • ☐ = ☐

new factor pair

120

Estimating with Decimals

ROUND the decimals first; then work the problem

Example

A. 5.8×4

is about $\boxed{6} \times 4$ is about $\boxed{24}$

Round the decimals to the ONES place and then solve

1. 2.3×7

is about $\boxed{} \times 7$ answer is about $\boxed{}$

2. 8.6×2

is about $\boxed{} \times 2$ answer is about $\boxed{}$

3. 6.2×5

is about $\boxed{} \times 5$ answer is about $\boxed{}$

4. 2.7×6

is about $\boxed{} \times 6$ answer is about $\boxed{}$

5. 1.8×1.9

is about $\boxed{} \times \boxed{}$ answer is about $\boxed{}$

6. 3.14×9

is about $\boxed{} \times 9$ answer is about $\boxed{}$

7. 5.3×2.8

is about $\boxed{} \times \boxed{}$ answer is about $\boxed{}$

8. $8.4 \div 2.3$

is about $\boxed{} \div \boxed{}$ answer is about $\boxed{}$

9. 3.6×7.4

is about $\boxed{} \times \boxed{}$ answer is about $\boxed{}$

10. $(4.8)^2$

$\boxed{}^2$ answer is about $\boxed{}$

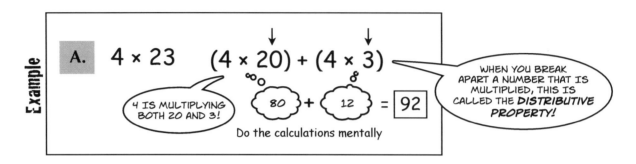

Distributive Property with Multiplication

Example

A. 4×23 $(4 \times 20) + (4 \times 3)$

4 IS MULTIPLYING BOTH 20 AND 3!

$80 + 12 = \boxed{92}$

Do the calculations mentally

WHEN YOU BREAK APART A NUMBER THAT IS MULTIPLIED, THIS IS CALLED THE *DISTRIBUTIVE PROPERTY!*

Break up the two-digit numbers and multiply each digit separately

Calculate final answers mentally

1. 3×14

$(3 \times 10) + (3 \times 4) = \boxed{}$

Do the calculations mentally

2. 2×46

$(2 \times 40) + (2 \times 6) = \boxed{}$

Do the calculations mentally

3. 8×13

$(8 \times 10) + (8 \times \boxed{}) = \boxed{}$

4. 2×67

$(2 \times 60) + (2 \times \boxed{}) = \boxed{}$

5. 4×24

$(4 \times \boxed{}) + (4 \times \boxed{}) = \boxed{}$

6. 2×78

$(2 \times \boxed{}) + (2 \times \boxed{}) = \boxed{}$

break up 78 into 70 + 8

7. 3×56

$(\boxed{} \times \boxed{}) + (\boxed{} \times \boxed{}) = \boxed{}$

8. 4×27

$(\boxed{} \times \boxed{}) + (\boxed{} \times \boxed{}) = \boxed{}$

9. 5×89

$(\boxed{} \times \boxed{}) + (\boxed{} \times \boxed{}) = \boxed{}$

10. 7×36

$(\boxed{} \times \boxed{}) + (\boxed{} \times \boxed{}) = \boxed{}$

122   break up 24 into 20 + 4

Distributive Property with Multiplication

Break up the two-digit numbers and multiply each digit separately

1. 3×17

$(3 \times 10) + (3 \times 7) = \boxed{}$

Do the calculations mentally

2. 2×97

$(2 \times 90) + (2 \times 7) = \boxed{}$

Do the calculations mentally

3. 5×79

$(5 \times \boxed{}) + (5 \times \boxed{}) = \boxed{}$

4. 8×23

$(8 \times \boxed{}) + (8 \times \boxed{}) = \boxed{}$

5. 9×34

$(9 \times \boxed{}) + (9 \times \boxed{}) = \boxed{}$

6. 4×36

$(4 \times \boxed{}) + (4 \times \boxed{}) = \boxed{}$

7. 6×27

$(6 \times \boxed{}) + (6 \times \boxed{}) = \boxed{}$

Do the calculations mentally

8. 4×84

$(\boxed{} \times \boxed{}) + (\boxed{} \times \boxed{}) = \boxed{}$

9. 6×73

$(\boxed{} \times \boxed{}) + (\boxed{} \times \boxed{}) = \boxed{}$

10. 7×28

$(\boxed{} \times \boxed{}) + (\boxed{} \times \boxed{}) = \boxed{}$

11. 8×59

$(\boxed{} \times \boxed{}) + (\boxed{} \times \boxed{}) = \boxed{}$

12. 9×65

$(\boxed{} \times \boxed{}) + (\boxed{} \times \boxed{}) = \boxed{}$

Distributive Property with Multiplication

Break up the two-digit numbers and multiply each digit separately

1. 3 × 18

(3 × 10) + (3 × 8) = ☐

Do the calculations mentally

2. 4 × 13

(☐ × ☐) + (☐ × ☐) = ☐

Do the calculations mentally

3. 7 × 17

(☐ × ☐) + (☐ × ☐) = ☐

4. 6 × 29

(☐ × ☐) + (☐ × ☐) = ☐

5. 8 × 48

(☐ × ☐) + (☐ × ☐) = ☐

6. 9 × 32

(☐ × ☐) + (☐ × ☐) = ☐

7. 5 × 76

(☐ × ☐) + (☐ × ☐) = ☐

8. 6 × 34

(☐ × ☐) + (☐ × ☐) = ☐

9. 7 × 28

(☐ × ☐) + (☐ × ☐) = ☐

10. 4 × 64

(☐ × ☐) + (☐ × ☐) = ☐

11. 8 × 73

(☐ × ☐) + (☐ × ☐) = ☐

12. 3 × 908

TREAT THE 9 & THE 0 AS A SINGLE NUMBER. WHAT NUMBER IS IT REALLY?

(☐ × ☐) + (☐ × ☐) = ☐

Distributive Property with Multiplication

Break up the two-digit numbers and multiply each digit separately

Do all calculations mentally

1. 4 × 17 = [ ]

2. 5 × 15 = [ ]

3. 6 × 17 = [ ]

4. 8 × 13 = [ ]

5. 3 × 19 = [ ]

6. 7 × 16 = [ ]

7. 9 × 17 = [ ]

8. 8 × 14 = [ ]

9. 7 × 19 = [ ]

10. 6 × 13 = [ ]

11. 2 × 29 = [ ]

12. 5 × 27 = [ ]

13. 6 × 29 = [ ]

14. 7 × 38 = [ ]

15. 9 × 23 = [ ]

16. 4 × 29 = [ ]

17. 7 × 24 = [ ]

18. 6 × 26 = [ ]

19. 3 × 28 = [ ]

20. 8 × 24 = [ ]

125

Estimating with Multiplication

Example

A.

round to the 10s place

$37 \rightarrow 40$

$\times 23 \rightarrow \times 20$

ESTIMATE EACH NUMBER BEFORE MULTIPLYING

$= \boxed{800}$

37 TIMES 23 IS ABOUT 800

Estimate by rounding both two-digit numbers and multiplying

ROUND THE 2-DIGIT NUMBERS TO THE NEAREST TEN!

1. $37 \rightarrow \boxed{}$
$\times 23 \rightarrow \times \boxed{}$ $= \boxed{}$

2. $52 \rightarrow \boxed{}$
$\times 68 \rightarrow \times \boxed{}$ $= \boxed{}$

3. $67 \rightarrow \boxed{}$
$\times 34 \rightarrow \times \boxed{}$ $= \boxed{}$

DO THE NEXT TWO PROBLEMS MENTALLY!

4. 83
$\times 17$ $= \boxed{}$

5. 49
$\times 8$ $= \boxed{}$

ROUND TO THE NEAREST 10!

ROUND THE 3-DIGIT NUMBERS TO THE NEAREST HUNDRED!

6. $287 \rightarrow \boxed{}$
$\times 12 \rightarrow \times \boxed{}$ $= \boxed{}$

7. $526 \rightarrow \boxed{}$
$\times 28 \rightarrow \times \boxed{}$ $= \boxed{}$

DO #8-10 MENTALLY IF YOU CAN!

8. $755 \rightarrow \boxed{}$
$\times 38 \rightarrow \times \boxed{}$ $= \boxed{}$

9. $439 \rightarrow \boxed{}$
$\times 18 \rightarrow \times \boxed{}$ $= \boxed{}$

10. $878 \rightarrow \boxed{}$
$\times 24 \rightarrow \times \boxed{}$ $= \boxed{}$

126

Estimating with Fractions

Example

> THE FRACTION HAS TO EQUAL 1/2 OR MORE TO RAISE THE WHOLE NUMBER UP ONE!

A. $2\frac{1}{4} \times 3\frac{4}{5}$

1/4 is less than 1/2, so we don't add 1 to the whole number

$\boxed{2} \times \boxed{4}$

4/5 is closer to 1, so you add 1 to the 3

Estimate by rounding the fractions before calculating the amounts

1. $4\frac{5}{6} \times 3\frac{1}{6}$

$\boxed{} \times \boxed{}$ answer is about $\boxed{}$

2. $5\frac{3}{4} \times 4\frac{9}{10}$

$\boxed{} \times \boxed{}$ answer is about $\boxed{}$

3. $7\frac{1}{3} \times 5\frac{6}{7}$

$\boxed{} \times \boxed{}$ answer is about $\boxed{}$

4. $11\frac{7}{9} \times 2\frac{4}{5}$

$\boxed{} \times \boxed{}$ answer is about $\boxed{}$

5. $15\frac{2}{7} \times 1\frac{7}{8}$

$\boxed{} \times \boxed{}$ answer is about $\boxed{}$

6. $19\frac{11}{12} \div 4\frac{1}{4}$

$\boxed{} \div \boxed{}$ answer is about $\boxed{}$

7. $25\frac{5}{7} + 3\frac{3}{10}$

$\boxed{} + \boxed{}$ answer is about $\boxed{}$

8. $14\frac{1}{3} - 2\frac{4}{5}$

$\boxed{} - \boxed{}$ answer is about $\boxed{}$

9. $34\frac{5}{7} \div 6\frac{2}{3}$

$\boxed{} \div \boxed{}$ answer is about $\boxed{}$

10. $20\frac{2}{5} \div 4\frac{7}{8}$

$\boxed{} \div \boxed{}$ answer is about $\boxed{}$

Four Times Table as Double-Double

Example

A. $4 \times ③ = $ 3 →(double)→ 6 →(double)→ 12

START WITH THE NUMBER 4 IS MULTIPLYING!

A NUMBER DOUBLED TWICE IS THE SAME AS TIMES 4!

Solve the 4 times table calculations by doing the DOUBLE-DOUBLE trick

1. $4 \times ② = $ 2 →(double)→ ☐ →(double)→ ☐

2. $4 \times ⑤ = $ 5 →(double)→ ☐ →(double)→ ☐

3. $4 \times ⑩ = $ 10 →(double)→ ☐ →(double)→ ☐

4. $4 \times ⑥ = $ 6 →(double)→ ☐ →(double)→ ☐

5. $4 \times ⑧ = $ 8 →(double)→ ☐ →(double)→ ☐

6. $4 \times ④ = $ 4 →(double)→ ☐ →(double)→ ☐

7. $4 \times ⑨ = $ 9 →(double)→ ☐ →(double)→ ☐

8. $4 \times ⑦ = $ 7 →(double)→ ☐ →(double)→ ☐

9. $4 \times ⑫ = $ 12 →(double)→ ☐ →(double)→ ☐

6 Times Table as Triple, Double

Example

A. $6 \times (10) =$ 10 $\xrightarrow{\text{times 3}}$ 30 $\xrightarrow{\text{times 2 (or double)}}$ 60

START WITH THE NUMBER 6 IS MULTIPLYING!

ANY NUMBER TIMES 3, TIMES 2 IS THE SAME AS TIMES 6!

Solve the 6 times table calculations by doing the TRIPLE-DOUBLE trick

1. $6 \times (2) =$ 2 $\xrightarrow{\text{x 3}}$ ☐ $\xrightarrow{\text{double}}$ ☐

2. $6 \times (5) =$ 5 $\xrightarrow{\text{x 3}}$ ☐ $\xrightarrow{\text{double}}$ ☐

3. $6 \times (3) =$ 3 $\xrightarrow{\text{x 3}}$ ☐ $\xrightarrow{\text{double}}$ ☐

4. $6 \times (8) =$ 8 $\xrightarrow{\text{x 3}}$ ☐ $\xrightarrow{\text{double}}$ ☐

5. $6 \times (6) =$ 6 $\xrightarrow{\text{x 3}}$ ☐ $\xrightarrow{\text{double}}$ ☐

6. $6 \times (9) =$ 9 $\xrightarrow{\text{x 3}}$ ☐ $\xrightarrow{\text{double}}$ ☐

7. $6 \times (7) =$ 7 $\xrightarrow{\text{x 3}}$ ☐ $\xrightarrow{\text{double}}$ ☐

8. $6 \times (4) =$ 4 $\xrightarrow{\text{x 3}}$ ☐ $\xrightarrow{\text{double}}$ ☐

9. $6 \times (12) =$ 12 $\xrightarrow{\text{x 3}}$ ☐ $\xrightarrow{\text{double}}$ ☐

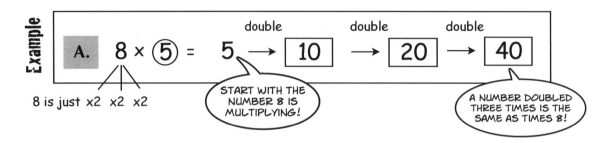

Example

A. $8 \times ⑤ =$ $5 \xrightarrow{\text{double}} \boxed{10} \xrightarrow{\text{double}} \boxed{20} \xrightarrow{\text{double}} \boxed{40}$

8 is just x2 x2 x2

START WITH THE NUMBER 8 IS MULTIPLYING!

A NUMBER DOUBLED THREE TIMES IS THE SAME AS TIMES 8!

Solve the 8 times table calculations by doing the DOUBLE-DOUBLE-DOUBLE trick

1. $8 \times ③ =$ $3 \xrightarrow{\text{double}} \boxed{} \xrightarrow{\text{double}} \boxed{} \xrightarrow{\text{double}} \boxed{}$

2. $8 \times ⑦ =$ $7 \xrightarrow{\text{double}} \boxed{} \xrightarrow{\text{double}} \boxed{} \xrightarrow{\text{double}} \boxed{}$

3. $8 \times ⑩ =$ $10 \xrightarrow{\text{double}} \boxed{} \xrightarrow{\text{double}} \boxed{} \xrightarrow{\text{double}} \boxed{}$

4. $8 \times ② =$ $2 \xrightarrow{\text{double}} \boxed{} \xrightarrow{\text{double}} \boxed{} \xrightarrow{\text{double}} \boxed{}$

5. $8 \times ④ =$ $4 \xrightarrow{\text{double}} \boxed{} \xrightarrow{\text{double}} \boxed{} \xrightarrow{\text{double}} \boxed{}$

6. $8 \times ⑥ =$ $6 \xrightarrow{\text{double}} \boxed{} \xrightarrow{\text{double}} \boxed{} \xrightarrow{\text{double}} \boxed{}$

7. $8 \times ⑧ =$ $8 \xrightarrow{\text{double}} \boxed{} \xrightarrow{\text{double}} \boxed{} \xrightarrow{\text{double}} \boxed{}$

8. $8 \times ⑨ =$ $9 \xrightarrow{\text{double}} \boxed{} \xrightarrow{\text{double}} \boxed{} \xrightarrow{\text{double}} \boxed{}$

9. $8 \times ⑫ =$ $12 \xrightarrow{\text{double}} \boxed{} \xrightarrow{\text{double}} \boxed{} \xrightarrow{\text{double}} \boxed{}$

12 Times Table as Triple-Double-Double

Example

A. $12 \times ②$ =

     times 3 (or triple)   double   double

$2 \rightarrow \boxed{6} \rightarrow \boxed{12} \rightarrow \boxed{24}$

12 is just ×3 ×2 ×2

START WITH THE NUMBER MULTIPLYING 12!

Solve the 12 times table calculations by doing the TRIPLE-DOUBLE-DOUBLE trick

		times 3 (= triple)	double	double
1.	$12 \times ③$ =	$3 \rightarrow \boxed{}$	$\rightarrow \boxed{}$	$\rightarrow \boxed{}$

		triple	double	double
2.	$12 \times ④$ =	$4 \rightarrow \boxed{}$	$\rightarrow \boxed{}$	$\rightarrow \boxed{}$
3.	$12 \times ②$ =	$2 \rightarrow \boxed{}$	$\rightarrow \boxed{}$	$\rightarrow \boxed{}$
4.	$12 \times ⑦$ =	$7 \rightarrow \boxed{}$	$\rightarrow \boxed{}$	$\rightarrow \boxed{}$
5.	$12 \times ⑩$ =	$10 \rightarrow \boxed{}$	$\rightarrow \boxed{}$	$\rightarrow \boxed{}$
6.	$12 \times ⑥$ =	$6 \rightarrow \boxed{}$	$\rightarrow \boxed{}$	$\rightarrow \boxed{}$
7.	$12 \times ⑨$ =	$9 \rightarrow \boxed{}$	$\rightarrow \boxed{}$	$\rightarrow \boxed{}$
8.	$12 \times ⑧$ =	$8 \rightarrow \boxed{}$	$\rightarrow \boxed{}$	$\rightarrow \boxed{}$
9.	$12 \times ⑫$ =	$12 \rightarrow \boxed{}$	$\rightarrow \boxed{}$	$\rightarrow \boxed{}$

Mixed Review

1. 7 . 5 4

2. 1 2 . 7 3

3. 5 6 . 8 4 5

Perform all four operations with the given numbers

		sum	product	difference	quotient
4.	30 5				
5.	20 4				
6.	12 3				
7.	14 2				

Break up the two-digit numbers and multiply each digit separately

8. 6 × 14

$(6 \times \boxed{}) + (6 \times \boxed{}) = \boxed{}$

9. 8 × 37

$(8 \times \boxed{}) + (8 \times \boxed{}) = \boxed{}$

Estimate by rounding the fractions before calculating the amounts

10. $5\frac{2}{3} \times 2\frac{1}{6}$

$\boxed{} \times \boxed{}$ answer is about $\boxed{}$

11. $14\frac{11}{12} \div 4\frac{3}{4}$

$\boxed{} \div \boxed{}$ answer is about $\boxed{}$

Answer Key

for

MathWise Number Sense

Visual Math and Counting

Page 1

Add the numbers on the dice

1. ⚃ ⚃ = **8**
2. ⚂ ⚁ = **5**
3. ⚃ ⚂ = **7**
4. ⚁ ⚁ ⚁ = **6**
5. ⚂ ⚂ ⚁ = **8**
6. ⚃ ⚁ ⚂ = **9**

Skip count forwards and backwards

7. Skip count by 2s
   1 3 **5** 7 **9** 11 **13** 15 **17** 19 **21** **23**

8. Skip count by 2s
   2 **4** **6** **8** **10** **12** **14** **16** **18** **20** **22** **24**

9. Skip count backwards by 2s
   30 **28** **26** **24** **22** **20** **18** **16** **14** **12** **10** **8**

Add the following coins

10. (10¢) (25¢) (5¢) = **40** ¢
11. (50¢) (25¢) (1¢) (1¢) = **77** ¢

1

Page 2

Add the numbers on the dice

1. ⚅ ⚅ = **12**
2. ⚄ ⚃ = **9**
3. ⚅ ⚄ = **11**
4. ⚃ ⚂ ⚅ = **13**
5. ⚄ ⚃ ⚁ = **10**
6. ⚁ ⚄ ⚃ = **11**

Skip count forwards and backwards

7. Skip count by 2s
   32 **34** 36 **38** **40** **42** 44 **46** **48** **50** **52** 54

8. Skip count by 3s
   3 **6** **9** 12 **15** **18** **21** 24 **27** **30** 33 **36**

9. Skip count by 10s
   17 **27** **37** **47** 57 **67** **77** **87** 97 **107** **117** **127**

Add the following coins

10. (25¢) (25¢) (25¢) (10¢) (5¢) = **90** ¢
11. (25¢) (10¢) (5¢) (5¢) = **45** ¢

2

Page 3

Add the numbers on the dice

1. ⚁ ⚃ = **6**
2. ⚂ ⚁ = **5**
3. ⚃ ⚃ = **8**
4. ⚄ ⚂ ⚂ = **11**
5. ⚃ ⚁ ⚃ = **10**
6. ⚅ ⚂ ⚂ = **12**

Skip count forwards and backwards

7. Skip count backwards by 2s
   24 **22** **20** **18** 16 **14** **12** **10** **8** **6** **4** **2**

8. Skip count forwards by 5s
   75 **80** **85** **90** **95** **100** **105** 110 **115** **120** **125**

9. Skip count forwards by 10s
   260 **270** **280** **290** **300** **310** **320** **330** **340** **350**

Add the following coins

10. (50¢) (50¢) (50¢) (10¢) (10¢) (10¢) (5¢) (5¢) (5¢) (1¢)
    (1¢) (1¢) (1¢) = **199** ¢

3

Page 4

Add the following dice

1. ⚅ ⚅ = **12**
2. ⚃ ⚃ ⚁ = **9**
3. ⚃ ⚅ ⚃ = **14**
4. ⚁ ⚁ ⚂ = **7**
5. ⚅ ⚅ ⚂ = **15**
6. ⚂ ⚂ ⚁ = **8**

Skip count forwards and backwards

7. Skip count backwards by 2s
   112 **110** **108** **106** **104** **102** **100** **98** **96** **94**

8. Skip count forwards by 25s (like counting by quarters with money)
   25 **50** **75** 100 **125** **150** **175** **200** **225** **250**

9. Skip count backwards by 10s
   113 **103** **93** **83** **73** **63** **53** **43** **33** **23**

Add the following coins

10. (25¢) (10¢) (10¢) (10¢) (10¢) (5¢) (5¢) (5¢) (5¢)
    35¢ **45** 55¢ **65** **70** **75** **80** **85** ¢

4

Making Tens

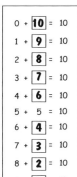

GIVE THE MISSING NUMBERS TO MAKE TENS

0 + **10** = 10
1 + **9** = 10
2 + **8** = 10
3 + **7** = 10
4 + **6** = 10
5 + 5 = 10
6 + **4** = 10
7 + **3** = 10
8 + **2** = 10
9 + **1** = 10
10 + **0** = 10

Sets are the reverse of each other!

1. 3 + **7** = 10
2. 6 + **4** = 10
3. 2 + **8** = 10
4. 1 + **9** = 10
5. 4 + **6** = 10
6. 7 + **3** = 10
7. 8 + **2** = 10
8. 5 + **5** = 10
9. 7 + **3** = 10
10. 6 + **4** = 10
11. 9 + **1** = 10
12. 8 + **2** = 10

SAME IDEA, BUT WITH 3 NUMBERS!

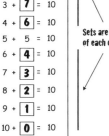

13. 3 + 2 + **5** = 10
14. 5 + 3 + **2** = 10
15. 2 + 5 + **3** = 10
16. 3 + 3 + **4** = 10

SIMILAR IDEA—BUT MAKE 20S!

17. 18 + **2** = 20
18. 14 + **6** = 20
19. 15 + **5** = 20
20. 17 + **3** = 20
21. 12 + **8** = 20
22. 13 + **7** = 20
23. 16 + **4** = 20
24. 11 + **9** = 20

© Peter Wise, 2016

5

Adding by Looking for Tens

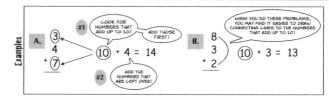

Examples

A. $\overset{3}{\underset{+7}{4}}$ #1 LOOK FOR NUMBERS THAT ADD UP TO 10! ADD THOSE FIRST! WHEN YOU DO THESE PROBLEMS, YOU MAY FIND IT EASIER TO DRAW CONNECTING LINES TO THE NUMBERS THAT ADD UP TO 10!

⑩ + 4 = 14

#2 ADD THE NUMBERS THAT ARE LEFT OVER!

B. $\overset{8}{\underset{+2}{3}}$ ⑩ + 3 = 13

Draw connector lines to the numbers that make 10; add the extra number(s) to get your final answer

IN THIS LAST COLUMN LOOK FOR THREE NUMBERS THAT ADD UP TO 10!

1.   4
     6
   + 9
   19

4.   5
     4
     3
   + 5
   17

7.   5
     3
     5
   + 7
   20

10. 5
     3
     2
   + 1
   11

2.   1
     8
   + 9
   18

5.   3
     6
     5
   + 4
   18

8.   2
     1
     4
   + 9
   16

11. 3
     3
     2
   + 4
   12

3.   5
     7
   + 3
   15

6.   8
     1
     3
   + 2
   14

9.   4
     7
     3
   + 6
   20

12. 3
     6
     8
   + 1
   18

© Peter Wise, 2016

6

Making Tens with Three Numbers

Example

A. 3 + 1 + **6** = 10

Make tens by finding the missing numbers

1. 2 + 7 + **1** = 10
2. 5 + 2 + **3** = 10
3. 2 + 4 + **4** = 10
4. 3 + 5 + **2** = 10
5. 1 + 3 + **6** = 10
6. 4 + 2 + **4** = 10
7. 2 + 5 + **3** = 10
8. 2 + 2 + **6** = 10
9. 6 + 2 + **2** = 10
10. 2 + 5 + **3** = 10

Make tens by finding the missing numbers (now with subtraction)

11. 3 - 1 + **8** = 10
12. 8 - 2 + **4** = 10
13. 8 - 3 + **5** = 10
14. 5 - 2 + **7** = 10
15. 8 - 5 + **7** = 10
16. 3 - 1 + **8** = 10
17. 9 - 2 + **3** = 10
18. 9 - 5 + **6** = 10

© Peter Wise, 2016

7

Making Thirty and Fifty

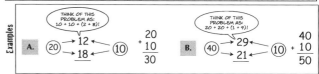

Examples

A. ㉒ → 12 ← ⑩ THINK OF THIS PROBLEM AS: 10 + 10 + (2 + 8)! → 18 ←
  $\begin{array}{r} 20 \\ +\ 10 \\ \hline 30 \end{array}$

B. ㊵ → 29 ← ⑩ THINK OF THIS PROBLEM AS: 20 + 20 + (1 + 9)! → 21 ←
  $\begin{array}{r} 40 \\ +\ 10 \\ \hline 50 \end{array}$

Make 30s by adding tens on the left and right columns

1.   1 3
   + 1 **7**
     3 0

6.   1 2
   + **18**
     3 0

2.   1 6
   + 1 **4**
     3 0

7.   1 9
   + **11**
     3 0

3.   1 5
   + 1 **5**
     3 0

8.   1 4
   + **16**
     3 0

4.   1 8
   + 1 **2**
     3 0

9.   1 3
   + **17**
     3 0

5.   1 1
   + 1 **9**
     3 0

10. 1 8
   + **12**
     3 0

Make 50s by adding tens on the left and right columns

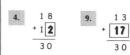
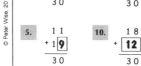

11. 2 3
   + 2 **7**
     5 0

16. 2 8
   + **22**
     5 0

12. 2 5
   + 2 **5**
     5 0

17. 3 7
   + **13**
     5 0

13. 2 6
   + 2 **4**
     5 0

18. 3 2
   + **18**
     5 0

14. 2 1
   + 2 **9**
     5 0

19. 3 6
   + **14**
     5 0

15. 2 2
   + 2 **8**
     5 0

20. 3 1
   + **19**
     5 0

© Peter Wise, 2016

8

Page 9

Adding Tens and Ones

Examples

A.	3 tens and 8	B.	14 tens and 8	C.	15 tens and 18
	3 tens = 30 + 8 = 38		14 tens = 140 + 8 = 148		15 tens = 150 + 18 = 168

Calculate the tens and the ones; then add them together

1. 4 tens and 3 = **43**
2. 4 tens and 13 = **53**

THERE IS ONE MORE TEN HERE!

3. 15 tens = **150**
4. 15 tens and 2 = **152**
5. 15 tens and 12 = **162**
6. 6 tens and 14 = **74**
7. 3 tens and 10 = **40**
8. 3 tens and 11 = **41**
9. 8 tens and 20 = **100**
10. 12 tens and 25 = **145**

TWO MORE TENS HERE!

11. 17 tens and 14 = **184**

12. 16 tens and 30 = **190**
13. 16 tens and 38 = **198**
14. 7 tens and 5 = **75**
15. 7 tens and 15 = **85**
16. 6 tens and 40 = **100**
17. 6 tens and 45 = **105**
18. 19 tens and 10 = **200**
19. 19 tens and 17 = **207**
20. 19 tens and 37 = **227**
21. 8 tens and 30 = **110**
22. 8 tens and 42 = **122**
23. 7 tens and 30 = **100**
24. 7 tens and 34 = **104**

© Peter Wise, 2016

9

Page 10

Adding Tens and Ones

1. 5 tens and 7 = **57**
2. 5 tens and 17 = **67**
3. 6 tens and 25 = **85**
4. 14 tens and 7 = **147**
5. 14 tens and 37 = **177**
6. 8 tens and 20 = **100**
7. 8 tens and 28 = **108**
8. 7 tens and 46 = **116**

9. 16 tens and 4 = **164**
10. 16 tens and 24 = **184**
11. 25 tens and 7 = **257**
12. 25 tens and 17 = **267**
13. 12 tens and 45 = **165**
14. 7 tens and 53 = **123**
15. 6 tens and 38 = **98**
16. 18 tens and 54 = **234**

FIND THE MISSING NUMBER! (MAKING 10S!)

17. 8 + **2** = 10
18. 13 + **7** = 20
19. 26 + **4** = 30

20. 4 + **6** = 10
21. 11 + **9** = 20
22. 23 + **7** = 30

23. 16 + **4** = 20
24. 12 + **8** = 20
25. 25 + **5** = 30

FIND THE MISSING NUMBERS IN THE SERIES!

26. 13 23 33 **43** **53** 63
27. 47 57 **67** **77** 87
28. 97 87 77 **67** **57** 47
29. 122 112 **102** **92** **82**

© Peter Wise, 2016

10

Page 11

Adding Tens and Ones

1. 6 tens and 2 = **62**
2. 6 tens and 12 = **72**
3. 6 tens and 22 = **82**
4. 16 tens and 2 = **162**
5. 16 tens and 42 = **202**
6. 5 tens and 37 = **87**
7. 9 tens and 15 = **105**
8. 7 tens and 39 = **109**

9. 2 tens and 37 = **57**
10. 3 tens and 71 = **101**
11. 11 tens and 8 = **118**
12. 11 tens and 28 = **138**
13. 1 ten and 14 = **24**
14. 7 tens and 57 = **127**
15. 8 tens and 35 = **115**
16. 18 tens and 35 = **215**

FIND THE MISSING NUMBER! (MAKING 10S!)

17. 12 + **8** = 20
18. 13 + **7** = 20
19. 3 + **17** = 20

20. 14 + **6** = 20
21. 4 + **16** = 20
22. 9 + **11** = 20

23. 2 + **18** = 20
24. 18 + **2** = 20
25. 13 + **7** = 20

FIND THE MISSING NUMBERS IN THE SERIES!

26. 72 82 92 **102** **112** 122
27. 65 55 **45** **35** 25
28. 79 69 59 **49** **39** 29
29. 117 107 **97** **87** **77**

© Peter Wise, 2016

11

Page 12

Adding Tens and Ones

1. 9 tens and 8 = **98**
2. 9 tens and 18 = **108**
3. 9 tens and 23 = **113**
4. 9 tens and 93 = **183**
5. 4 tens and 42 = **82**
6. 3 tens and 61 = **91**
7. 13 tens and 27 = **157**
8. 8 tens and 51 = **131**

9. 19 tens and 7 = **197**
10. 19 tens and 27 = **217**
11. 28 tens and 4 = **284**
12. 28 tens and 24 = **304**
13. 4 tens and 125 = **165**
14. 5 tens and 139 = **189**
15. 12 tens and 45 = **165**
16. 8 tens and 71 = **151**

FIND THE MISSING NUMBER! (MAKING 10S!)

17. 7 + **23** = 30
18. 12 + **18** = 30
19. 6 + **24** = 30

20. 3 + **47** = 50
21. 41 + **9** = 50
22. 31 + **19** = 50

23. 94 + **6** = 100
24. 84 + **16** = 100
25. 89 + **11** = 100

FIND THE MISSING NUMBERS IN THE SERIES!

26. 14 24 34 **44** **54** 64
27. 88 98 **108** **118** 128
28. 92 82 72 **62** **52** 42
29. 133 123 **113** **103** **93**

© Peter Wise, 2016

12

Draw connector lines to the numbers that make 10, then add

1.
5
7
2   **10**
+ 5
19

2.
2
4
3   **10**
+ 6
15

3.
8
1
2   **10**
+ 6
17

4.
3
9
5   **10**
+ 1
18

Make tens by finding the missing numbers

5. 5 + 3 + **2** = 10

7. 2 + 3 + **5** = 10

6. 3 + 4 + **3** = 10

8. 2 + 4 + **4** = 10

Make 30s by finding the missing numbers

9.
1 2
+ 1 **8**
3 0

10.
1 6
+ 1 **4**
3 0

11.
1 3
+ **1 7**
3 0

12.
1 1
+ **1 9**
3 0

Calculate the tens and the ones; then add them together

13. 3 tens and 2 = **32**

16. 12 tens and 14 = **134**

14. 3 tens and 12 = **42**

17. 9 tens and 56 = **146**

15. 6 tens and 15 = **75**

18. 8 tens and 25 = **105**

© Peter Wise, 2016

13

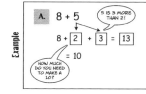

Example

A. 8 + 5

5 IS 3 MORE THAN 2!

8 + **2** + **3** = **13**

= 10

HOW MUCH DO YOU NEED TO MAKE A 10?

Break up numbers to make 10s (or multiples of 10)!

Sometimes referred to as Number Decomposition

You are really rearranging numbers to make 10s

Add numbers by making 10s

1. 7 + 5
7 + **3** + **2** = **12**
= 10

5. 2 + 9
2 + **8** + **1** = **11**
= 10

2. 5 + 9
5 + **5** + **4** = **14**
= 10

6. 7 + 9
7 + **3** + **6** = **16**
= 10

3. 3 + 8
3 + **7** + **1** = **11**
= 10

7. 8 + 15
8 + **2** + **13** = **23**
= 10

4. 8 + 6
8 + **2** + **4** = **14**
= 10

8. 6 + 28
6 + **4** + **24** = **34**
= 10

© Peter Wise, 2016

14

Example

A. 7 + 5
7 + **3** + **2** = **12**
= 10

Add the following numbers by making 10s

1. 8 + 3
8 + **2** + **1** = **11**
= 10

6. 4 + 8
4 + **6** + **2** = **12**
= 10

2. 9 + 4
9 + **1** + **3** = **13**
= 10

7. 6 + 7
6 + **4** + **3** = **13**
= 10

3. 8 + 6
8 + **2** + **4** = **14**
= 10

8. 9 + 6
9 + **1** + **5** = **15**
= 10

4. 5 + 8
5 + **5** + **3** = **13**
= 10

9. 8 + 9
8 + **2** + **7** = **17**
= 10

5. 7 + 8
7 + **3** + **5** = **15**
= 10

10. 4 + 7
4 + **6** + **1** = **11**
= 10

© Peter Wise, 2016

15

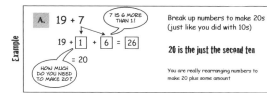
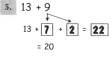

Example

A. 19 + 7

7 IS 6 MORE THAN 1!

19 + **1** + **6** = **26**

= 20

HOW MUCH DO YOU NEED TO MAKE 20?

Break up numbers to make 20s (just like you did with 10s)

20 is the just the second ten

You are really rearranging numbers to make 20 plus some amount

Add the following numbers by making 20s

1. 16 + 5
16 + **4** + **1** = **21**
answer
= 20

5. 13 + 9
13 + **7** + **2** = **22**
= 20

2. 19 + 8
19 + **1** + **7** = **27**
= 20

6. 18 + 7
18 + **2** + **5** = **25**
= 20

3. 14 + 8
14 + **6** + **2** = **22**
= 20

7. 17 + 6
17 + **3** + **3** = **23**
= 20

4. 17 + 9
17 + **3** + **6** = **26**
= 20

8. 15 + 7
15 + **5** + **2** = **22**
= 20

© Peter Wise, 2016

16

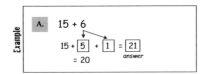

How Much More Than 20?

Example

A. 15 + 6

15 + $\boxed{5}$ + $\boxed{1}$ = $\boxed{21}$
= 20   answer

Add the following numbers by making 20s

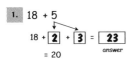

1. 18 + 5

   18 + $\boxed{2}$ + $\boxed{3}$ = $\boxed{23}$
   = 20   answer

2. 17 + 9

   17 + $\boxed{3}$ + $\boxed{6}$ = $\boxed{26}$
   = 20

3. 15 + 7

   15 + $\boxed{5}$ + $\boxed{2}$ = $\boxed{22}$
   = 20

4. 14 + 9

   14 + $\boxed{6}$ + $\boxed{3}$ = $\boxed{23}$
   = 20

5. 19 + 7

   19 + $\boxed{1}$ + $\boxed{6}$ = $\boxed{26}$
   = 20

6. 13 + 8

   13 + $\boxed{7}$ + $\boxed{1}$ = $\boxed{21}$
   = 20

7. 18 + 9

   18 + $\boxed{2}$ + $\boxed{7}$ = $\boxed{27}$
   = 20

8. 17 + 8

   17 + $\boxed{3}$ + $\boxed{5}$ = $\boxed{25}$
   = 20

© Peter Wise, 2016

17

Adding Neighbors (Close Numbers)

Add the following close numbers

1. 7 + 7 = $\boxed{14}$

   7 + 8 = $\boxed{15}$

2. 6 + 6 = $\boxed{12}$

   6 + 7 = $\boxed{13}$

3. 8 + 8 = $\boxed{16}$

   8 + 9 = $\boxed{17}$

4. 3 + 3 = $\boxed{6}$

   3 + 4 = $\boxed{7}$

5. 5 + 5 = $\boxed{10}$

   5 + 6 = $\boxed{11}$

6. 9 + 9 = $\boxed{18}$

   9 + 8 = $\boxed{17}$

7. 12 + 12 = $\boxed{24}$

   12 + 13 = $\boxed{25}$

8. 11 + 11 = $\boxed{22}$

   11 + 12 = $\boxed{23}$

9. 15 + 15 = $\boxed{30}$

   15 + 16 = $\boxed{31}$

10. 14 + 14 = $\boxed{28}$

    14 + 15 = $\boxed{29}$

Skip count

11. By 20s: 20 40 **60 80 100 120 140 160 180**

12. By 30s: 30 60 **90 120 150 180 210 240 270**

© Peter Wise, 2016

18

One More 10 for the Fives

Example

A. $\boxed{10}$ both fives add up to 10

35 + 35 = 70

$\boxed{60}$ 30 + 30 = 60   Now add the numbers in the boxes: 60 + 10 = 70

Adding two fives gives you one more ten

Find the sums of the following numbers

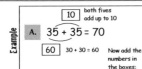

$\boxed{10}$ ADD THE 5'S

1. 15 + 15 = $\boxed{30}$

   $\boxed{20}$ ADD THE 10'S   ADD THE AMOUNTS IN THE TWO BOXES!

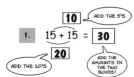

$\boxed{10}$ add the 5s

2. 25 + 25 = $\boxed{50}$

   $\boxed{40}$ add the tens place

$\boxed{10}$ add the 5s

3. 45 + 45 = $\boxed{90}$

   $\boxed{80}$ add the tens place

$\boxed{10}$ add the 5s

4. 75 + 75 = $\boxed{150}$

   $\boxed{140}$ add the tens place

$\boxed{10}$ ones place

5. 55 + 55 = $\boxed{110}$

   $\boxed{100}$ tens place

$\boxed{10}$ fives

6. 95 + 95 = $\boxed{190}$

   $\boxed{180}$ tens place

$\boxed{10}$ fives

7. 65 + 65 = $\boxed{130}$

   $\boxed{120}$ tens place

$\boxed{10}$ fives

8. 45 + 35 = $\boxed{80}$

   $\boxed{70}$ tens place

$\boxed{10}$ fives

9. 35 + 75 = $\boxed{110}$

   $\boxed{100}$ add the tens place

© Peter Wise, 2016

19

Add More Tens

Example

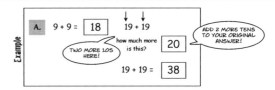

A. 9 + 9 = $\boxed{18}$ 19 + 19

TWO MORE 10S HERE!

how much more is this? $\boxed{20}$

ADD 2 MORE TENS TO YOUR ORIGINAL ANSWER!

19 + 19 = $\boxed{38}$

Add the original numbers, add the additional tens, solve the new problems

1. 7 + 2 = $\boxed{9}$ 17 + 12

   how much more is this? $\boxed{20}$

   17 + 12 = $\boxed{29}$

2. 3 + 5 = $\boxed{8}$ 13 + 15

   how much more is this? $\boxed{20}$

   13 + 15 = $\boxed{28}$

3. 6 + 9 = $\boxed{15}$ 26 + 19

   how much more is this? $\boxed{30}$

   26 + 19 = $\boxed{45}$

4. 5 + 8 = $\boxed{13}$ 25 + 28

   how much more is this? $\boxed{40}$

   25 + 28 = $\boxed{53}$

5. 12 + 4 = $\boxed{16}$ 22 + 14

   how much more is this? $\boxed{20}$

   22 + 14 = $\boxed{36}$

6. 17 + 7 = $\boxed{24}$ 37 + 27

   how much more is this? $\boxed{40}$

   37 + 27 = $\boxed{64}$

7. 15 + 6 = $\boxed{21}$ 35 + 16

   how much more is this? $\boxed{30}$

   35 + 16 = $\boxed{51}$

8. 14 + 5 = $\boxed{19}$ 44 + 15

   how much more is this? $\boxed{40}$

   44 + 15 = $\boxed{59}$

© Peter Wise, 2016

20

Add More Tens

Add the original numbers, add the additional tens, solve the new problems

1. $5 + 6 =$ **11** $15 + 16$
   how much more is this? **20**
   $15 + 16 =$ **31**

2. $8 + 8 =$ **16** $18 + 28$
   how much more is this? **30**
   $18 + 28 =$ **46**

3. $7 + 7 =$ **14** $27 + 27$
   how much more is this? **40**
   $27 + 27 =$ **54**

4. $13 + 6 =$ **19** $23 + 26$
   how much more is this? **30**
   $23 + 26 =$ **49**

5. $9 + 9 =$ **18** $39 + 39$
   how much more is this? **60**
   $39 + 39 =$ **78**

6. $14 + 5 =$ **19** $34 + 25$
   how much more is this? **40**
   $34 + 25 =$ **59**

7. $6 + 7 =$ **13** $26 + 7$
   how much more is this? **20**
   $26 + 7 =$ **33**

8. $19 + 7 =$ **26** $29 + 27$
   how much more is this? **30**
   $29 + 27 =$ **56**

9. $15 + 9 =$ **24** $25 + 39$
   how much more is this? **40**
   $25 + 39 =$ **64**

10. $18 + 7 =$ **25** $48 + 27$
    how much more is this? **50**
    $48 + 27 =$ **75**

21

Adding as Doubles +1 or -1

Example

A. $4 + 5 =$ $\boxed{4} + \boxed{4} + 1 = 9$ Double the lower number + 1

5 IS JUST ONE MORE THAN 4!

$\boxed{5} + \boxed{5} - 1 = 9$ Double the higher number - 1

Add the following close numbers

1. $4 + 5 =$
   Double the lower number $\boxed{4} + \boxed{4} + 1 = \boxed{9}$
   Double the higher number $\boxed{5} + \boxed{5} - 1 = \boxed{9}$

2. $6 + 7 =$
   Double the lower number $\boxed{6} + \boxed{6} + 1 = \boxed{13}$

3. $8 + 9 =$
   Double the higher number $\boxed{9} + \boxed{9} - 1 = \boxed{17}$

4. $7 + 8 =$
   Double the higher number $\boxed{8} + \boxed{8} - 1 = \boxed{15}$

5. $10 + 11 =$
   $\boxed{10} + \boxed{10} + 1 = \boxed{21}$

6. $15 + 16 =$
   $\boxed{15} + \boxed{15} + 1 = \boxed{31}$

Skip count

11. By 8s: 8 **16 24 32 40 48 56**
    8 IS "UP A 10, DOWN A 2"!

12. By 12s: 12 **24 36 48 60 72 84**
    12 IS "UP A 10, UP A 2"!

22

Adding Twins and Close Numbers

Add the following close numbers

1. $4 + 4 =$ **8**
   $4 + 5 =$ **9**
   1 more

2. $3 + 3 =$ **6**
   $3 + 5 =$ **8**
   2 more

3. $7 + 7 =$ **14**
   $7 + 8 =$ **15**
   1 more

4. $6 + 6 =$ **12**
   $6 + 8 =$ **14**
   2 more

5. $8 + 8 =$ **16**
   $8 + 9 =$ **17**
   1 more

6. $5 + 5 =$ **10**
   $5 + 7 =$ **12**
   2 more

7. $7 + 7 =$ **14**
   $7 + 9 =$ **16**
   2 more

8. $6 + 6 =$ **12**
   $6 + 7 =$ **13**
   1 more

9. $5 + 5 =$ **10**
   $5 + 8 =$ **13**
   3 more

10. $9 + 9 =$ **18**
    $9 + 11 =$ **20**
    2 more

23

Doubling Numbers

Add the following pairs of numbers

1. $\begin{array}{r} 7 \\ + 7 \\ \hline \end{array}$ **14**

2. $\begin{array}{r} 9 \\ + 9 \\ \hline \end{array}$ **18**

3. $\begin{array}{r} 8 \\ + 8 \\ \hline \end{array}$ **16**

4. $\begin{array}{r} 6 \\ + 6 \\ \hline \end{array}$ **12**

5. $\begin{array}{r} 17 \\ + 17 \\ \hline \end{array}$ **34**

6. $\begin{array}{r} 19 \\ + 19 \\ \hline \end{array}$ **38**

7. $\begin{array}{r} 14 \\ + 14 \\ \hline \end{array}$ **28**

8. $\begin{array}{r} 15 \\ + 15 \\ \hline \end{array}$ **30**

9. $\begin{array}{r} 28 \\ + 28 \\ \hline \end{array}$ **56**

10. $\begin{array}{r} 24 \\ + 24 \\ \hline \end{array}$ **48**

11. $\begin{array}{r} 26 \\ + 26 \\ \hline \end{array}$ **52**

12. $\begin{array}{r} 39 \\ + 39 \\ \hline \end{array}$ **78**

13. $\begin{array}{r} 34 \\ + 34 \\ \hline \end{array}$ **68**

14. $\begin{array}{r} 27 \\ + 27 \\ \hline \end{array}$ **54**

15. $\begin{array}{r} 18 \\ + 18 \\ \hline \end{array}$ **36**

16. $\begin{array}{r} 36 \\ + 36 \\ \hline \end{array}$ **72**

17. $\begin{array}{r} 45 \\ + 45 \\ \hline \end{array}$ **90**

18. $\begin{array}{r} 38 \\ + 38 \\ \hline \end{array}$ **76**

19. $\begin{array}{r} 29 \\ + 29 \\ \hline \end{array}$ **58**

20. $\begin{array}{r} 47 \\ + 47 \\ \hline \end{array}$ **94**

24

Doubling Numbers

Add the following pairs of numbers mentally, watch for carries

1. $+\dfrac{16}{16}$ = **32**	2. $+\dfrac{19}{19}$ = **38**	3. $+\dfrac{14}{14}$ = **28**	4. $+\dfrac{18}{18}$ = **36**
5. $+\dfrac{17}{17}$ = **34**	6. $+\dfrac{15}{15}$ = **30**	7. $+\dfrac{23}{23}$ = **46**	8. $+\dfrac{27}{27}$ = **54**
9. $+\dfrac{26}{26}$ = **52**	10. $+\dfrac{29}{29}$ = **58**	11. $+\dfrac{28}{28}$ = **56**	12. $+\dfrac{32}{32}$ = **64**
13. $+\dfrac{37}{37}$ = **74**	14. $+\dfrac{36}{36}$ = **72**	15. $+\dfrac{34}{34}$ = **68**	16. $+\dfrac{35}{35}$ = **70**
17. $+\dfrac{49}{49}$ = **98**	18. $+\dfrac{45}{45}$ = **90**	19. $+\dfrac{47}{47}$ = **94**	20. $+\dfrac{48}{48}$ = **96**

© Peter Wise, 2016

25

Doubling Numbers

Double the following numbers

**5 or more in the ONES place will give you a CARRY
if you carry, add one more to the TENS place**

1.	12 → **24**	13.	31 → **62**
2.	14 → **28**	14.	36 → **72**
3.	15 → **30**	15.	34 → **68**
4.	17 → **34**	16.	35 → **70**
5.	13 → **26**	17.	16 → **32**
6.	19 → **38**	18.	42 → **84**
7.	18 → **36**	19.	47 → **94**
8.	26 → **52**	20.	43 → **86**
9.	23 → **46**	21.	38 → **76**
10.	27 → **54**	22.	46 → **92**
11.	22 → **44**	23.	37 → **74**
12.	29 → **58**	24.	49 → **98**

13. $\underset{\text{5 more}}{31}$ → **62** when 5 more is doubled, it becomes 10 more

26

Doubling Numbers

Add the following twin numbers

1.	6 + 6 =	**12**	11.	23 + 23 =	**46**
2.	8 + 8 =	**16**	12.	34 + 34 =	**68**
3.	4 + 4 =	**8**	13.	17 + 17 =	**34**
4.	7 + 7 =	**14**	14.	41 + 41 =	**82**
5.	9 + 9 =	**18**	15.	70 + 70 =	**140**
6.	12 + 12 =	**24**	16.	74 + 74 =	**148**
7.	11 + 11 =	**22**	17.	26 + 26 =	**52**
8.	15 + 15 =	**30**	18.	38 + 38 =	**76**
9.	13 + 13 =	**26**	19.	24 + 24 =	**48**
10.	14 + 14 =	**28**	20.	108 + 108 =	**216**

Review Problems

21.	14 + **6** = 20	24.	4 tens and 7 = **47**
22.	17 + **3** = 20	25.	4 tens and 17 = **57**
23.	12 + **8** = 20	26.	7 tens and 25 = **95**

© Peter Wise, 2016

27

Doubling Numbers Left to Right

If the 1s place number is 5 or more add one to the tens place

$$18 + 18 = 3\ 6$$

1 + 1 = 2, but you need to add one more because of the carry.

#1 Check if the 1s place digit is 5 or more

#2 Add the TENS place FIRST, but add one if the tens place number is 5 or more

#3 Double the ONES place number, but just write the last digit (1s place)

A. $18 + 18 = 3\ 6$

5 or more in the 1s place will give you a CARRY. The 10s place will go UP ONE

Example

Double the following numbers by going LEFT to RIGHT

1. 17 + 17 =
will you have a carry? **(y)** n
add the TENS place
add 1 more if a carry → **3** **4**
add the ONES place
LAST digit only

2. 13 + 13 =
will you have a carry? y **(n)**
add the TENS place
add 1 more if a carry → **2** **6**
add the ONES place
LAST digit only

3. 19 + 19 =
will you have a carry? **(y)** n
add the TENS place
add 1 more if a carry → **3** **8**
add the ONES place
LAST digit only

4. 26 + 26 =
will you have a carry? **(y)** n
add the TENS place
add 1 more if a carry → **5** **2**
add the ONES place
LAST digit only

5. 48 + 48 =
will you have a carry? **(y)** n
add the TENS place
add 1 more if a carry → **9** **6**
add the ONES place

6. 45 + 45 =
will you have a carry? **(y)** n
add the TENS place
add 1 more if a carry → **9** **0**
add the ONES place

© Peter Wise, 2016

28

Doubling Numbers Left to Right

Double the following numbers by going LEFT to RIGHT

1. 18 + 18 =

add the TENS place
add 1 more if a carry → | 3 | 6 |

add the ONES place
LAST digit only

2. 35 + 35 =

add the TENS place
add 1 more if a carry → | 7 | 0 |

add the ONES place
LAST digit only

3. 24 + 24 =

add the TENS place
add 1 more if a carry → | 4 | 8 |

add the ONES place

4. 43 + 43 =

add the TENS place
add 1 more if a carry → | 8 | 6 |

add the ONES place

5. 29 + 29 =

add the TENS place
add 1 more if a carry → | 5 | 8 |

add the ONES place

6. 32 + 32 =

add the TENS place
add 1 more if a carry → | 6 | 4 |

add the ONES place
LAST digit only

7. 27 + 27 =

add the TENS place
add 1 more if a carry → | 5 | 4 |

add the ONES place

8. 49 + 49 =

add the TENS place
add 1 more if a carry → | 9 | 8 |

add the ONES place

9. 36 + 36 =

add the TENS place
add 1 more if a carry → | 7 | 2 |

add the ONES place

10. 46 + 46 =

add the TENS place
add 1 more if a carry → | 9 | 2 |

add the ONES place

29

Doubling Numbers Left to Right

Example

1 + 1 = 2, but you need to add one more because of the carry.

A. 16 + 16 = 3 6

5 or more in the 1s place will give you a CARRY. The 10s place will go UP ONE.

If the is place number is 5-9 add one more to the tens place

#1 Check if the 1s place digit is 5 or more

#2 Add the TENS place FIRST, but add one if the tens place number is 5 or more

#3 Double the ONES place number, but just write the last digit (1s place)

Double the following numbers by going LEFT to RIGHT

1. 28 + 28 = **56**
2. 34 + 34 = **68**
3. 18 + 18 = **36**
4. 46 + 46 = **92**
5. 27 + 27 = **54**
6. 19 + 19 = **38**
7. 35 + 35 = **70**
8. 47 + 47 = **94**
9. 42 + 42 = **84**

10. 17 + 17 = **34**
11. 26 + 26 = **52**
12. 44 + 44 = **88**
13. 15 + 15 = **30**
14. 41 + 41 = **82**
15. 32 + 32 = **64**
16. 28 + 28 = **56**
17. 29 + 29 = **58**
18. 137 + 137 = **274**

30

Doubling Three-Digit Numbers

Double the following numbers by going LEFT to RIGHT

1. 178 + 178 =

Does the 10s place have a carry? (y) n   LAST digit only / LAST digit only

add the 100s place
add 1 more if a carry → | 3 | 5 | 6 |

Does the 1s place have a carry? (y) n

add the 10s place
add 1 more if a carry

add the ONES place
LAST digit only

2. 287 + 287 =

Does the 10s place have a carry? (y) n   LAST digit only / LAST digit only

add the 100s place
add 1 more if a carry → | 5 | 7 | 4 |

Does the 1s place have a carry? (y) n

add the 10s place
add 1 more if a carry

add the ONES place
LAST digit only

3. 346 + 346 =

Does the 10s place have a carry? y (n)   LAST digit only / LAST digit only

add the 100s place
add 1 more if a carry → | 6 | 9 | 2 |

Does the 1s place have a carry? (y) n

add the 10s place
add 1 more if a carry

add the ONES place
LAST digit only

4. 465 + 465 =

Does the 10s place have a carry? (y) n   LAST digit only / LAST digit only

add the 100s place
add 1 more if a carry → | 9 | 3 | 0 |

Does the 1s place have a carry? (y) n

add the 10s place
add 1 more if a carry

add the ONES place
LAST digit only

Try doubling these numbers mentally

5. 1 7 6
↓ ↓ ↓
| 3 | 5 | 2 |

6. 4 1 8
↓ ↓ ↓
| 8 | 3 | 6 |

7. 2 9 7
↓ ↓ ↓
| 5 | 9 | 4 |

31

Doubling Practice

Double the following numbers

1. 15 + 15 = **30**
2. 35 + 35 = **70**
3. 17 + 17 = **34**
4. 37 + 37 = **74**
5. 19 + 19 = **38**
6. 21 + 21 = **42**
7. 16 + 16 = **32**
8. 36 + 36 = **72**
9. 18 + 18 = **36**
10. 28 + 28 = **56**

Add the 100s first / Add the 32s together / 100 + 100, 32 + 32
11. 132 + 132 = **264**

Add the hundreds first / Add the 15s together / 200 + 200, 15 + 15
12. 215 + 215 = **430**

13. 127 + 127 = **254**
14. 346 + 346 = **692**
15. 138 + 138 = **276**
16. 419 + 419 = **838**
17. 345 + 345 = **690**
18. 243 + 243 = **486**
19. 428 + 428 = **856**
20. 349 + 349 = **698**

32

Adding Even and Odd Numbers

if both are the same, you get an even number		if one is even and the other is odd, you get an odd number	
Even + Even = EVEN	2 + 6 = 8	Even + Odd = ODD	2 + 3 = 5
	E + E = E		E + O = O
Odd + Odd = EVEN	3 + 7 = 10	Odd + Even = ODD	5 + 2 = 7
	O + O = E		O + E = O

Put "E" for EVEN and "O" for ODD and find the sums

1. 5 + 7 = **12**
   O O E

   PUT "E" OR "O" FOR EVEN AND ODD HERE!

2. 4 + 1 = **5**
   E O O

3. 11 + 6 = **17**
   O E O

4. 1 + 7 = **8**
   O O E

5. 9 + 9 = **18**
   O O E

6. 1 + 5 = **6**
   O O E

7. 9 + 1 = **10**
   O O E

8. 7 + 7 = **14**
   O O E

9. 7 + 7 + 7 = **21**
   O O O O

33

Double the Between Number

Example

A. 4 + 6 = [10]

4 [5] 6 =

Double the between number | The between number is 5 | Two times 5 is 10

Every time you add it's the same as double the middle

Find the between (middle) number and double it

1. 2 + 4
   2 [3] 4 = **6**
   Double

2. 5 + 7
   5 [6] 7 = **12**
   Double

3. 6 + 8
   6 [7] 8 = **14**
   Double

4. 5 + 3
   5 [4] 3 = **8**
   Double

5. 9 + 7
   9 [8] 7 = **16**
   Double

6. 11 + 9
   11 [10] 9 = **20**
   Double

7. 13 + 11
   13 [12] 11 = **24**
   Double

8. 24 + 26
   24 [25] 26 = **50**
   Double

9. 10 + 12
   10 [11] 12 = **22**
   Double

10. 13 + 15
    13 [14] 15 = **28**
    Double

11. 29 + 31
    29 [30] 31 = **60**
    Double

12. 15 + 17
    15 [16] 17 = **32**
    Double

34

Double the Between Number

Find the middle number and double it

1. 14 + 16
   14 [15] 16 = **30**
   Double

2. 16 + 18
   16 [17] 18 = **34**
   Double

   WHEN BOTH NUMBERS ARE INCREASED BY 2, WHAT HAPPENS TO THE SUM?

3. 22 + 24
   22 [23] 24 = **46**

4. 24 + 26
   24 [25] 26 = **50**

5. 12 + 14
   12 [13] 14 = **26**

6. 33 + 35
   33 [34] 35 = **68**

7. 17 + 19
   17 [18] 19 = **36**

8. 19 + 21
   19 [20] 21 = **40**

9. 36 + 38
   36 [37] 38 = **74**

10. 25 + 27
    25 [26] 27 = **52**

11. 42 + 44
    42 [43] 44 = **86**

12. 47 + 49
    47 [48] 49 = **96**

35

Double the Between Number

Find the middle number and double it

1. 12 + 14
   12 [13] 14 = **26**
   Double

2. 31 + 33
   31 [32] 33 = **64**
   Double

   WHAT DO YOU NOTICE ABOUT THE MIDDLE NUMBER AND THE MEAN (AVERAGE)?

   WHAT CONCLUSION CAN YOU MAKE ABOUT ADDING AVERAGES (MEANS)?

3. 39 + 41
   39 [40] 41 = **80**

4. 55 + 57
   55 [56] 57 = **112**

5. 44 + 46
   44 [45] 46 = **90**

6. 27 + 29
   27 [28] 29 = **56**

7. 85 + 87
   85 [86] 87 = **172**

8. 37 + 39
   37 [38] 39 = **76**

9. 25 + 23
   25 [24] 23 = **48**

10. 32 + 34
    32 [33] 34 = **66**

11. 28 + 26
    28 [27] 26 = **54**

12. 46 + 48
    46 [47] 48 = **94**

36

© Peter Wise, 2016

Halving Numbers

Cut the following numbers in half

1. 8 → **4**
   cut the number in half (divide by 2)
2. 12 → **6**
3. 10 → **5**
4. 14 → **7**
5. 18 → **9**
6. 16 → **8**
7. 22 → **11**
8. 66 → **33**
9. 44 → **22**
10. 28 → **14**
11. 24 → **12**
12. 240 → **120**
13. 180 → **90**
14. 220 → **110**
15. 460 → **230**
16. 880 → **440**
17. 882 → **441**
18. 260 → **130**
19. 840 → **420**
20. 682 → **341**

Halving Numbers

Cut the following numbers in half

1. 18 → **9**
   cut the number in half (divide by 2)
2. 22 → **11**   4 more
3. 26 → **13**   when 4 more is halved, it becomes 2 more
4. 30 → **15**
5. 28 → **14**
6. 34 → **17**
7. 42 → **21**
8. 64 → **32**
9. 36 → **18**
10. 38 → **19**
11. 68 → **34**
12. 46 → **23**
13. 42 → **21**
14. 32 → **16**
15. 70 → **35**
16. 90 → **45**
17. 150 → **75**
18. 120 → **60**
19. 240 → **120**
20. 1050 → **525**

Halving Numbers

Cut the following numbers in half

1. 16 → **8**
   cut the number in half (divide by 2)
2. 12 → **6**
3. 14 → **7**
4. 18 → **9**
5. 24 → **12**
6. 28 → **14**
7. 46 → **23**
8. 64 → **32**
9. 32 → **16**
10. 34 → **17**
11. 264 → **132**
12. 428 → **214**
13. 646 → **323**
14. 82 → **41**
15. 22 → **11**
16. 68 → **34**
17. 206 → **103**
18. 408 → **204**
19. 614 → **307**
20. 812 → **406**

Mixed Review

Add the following close numbers

1. $6 + 6 =$ **12** $6 + 7 =$ **13**
2. $8 + 8 =$ **16** $8 + 9 =$ **17**
3. $7 + 7 =$ **14** $7 + 8 =$ **15**

Add numbers by making 10s

4. $8 + 5$
   $8 + \boxed{2} + \boxed{3} = $ **13**
   $= 10$
5. $7 + 4$
   $7 + \boxed{3} + \boxed{1} = $ **11**
   $= 10$
6. $9 + 3$
   $9 + \boxed{1} + \boxed{2} = $ **12**
   $= 10$

Add the original numbers, add the additional tens, solve the new problems

7. $9 + 4 =$ **13** $19 + 14$
   how much more is this? **20**
   $19 + 14 =$ **33**
8. $8 + 7 =$ **15** $28 + 27$
   how much more is this? **40**
   $28 + 27 =$ **55**

Double the following numbers

9. $14 →$ **28**
10. $17 →$ **34**
11. $19 →$ **38**

Cut the following numbers in half

12. $36 →$ **18**
13. $52 →$ **26**
13. $76 →$ **38**

Halving Numbers when the 10s Digit is Odd

Method #1: Breaking up the number into 10s and 1s

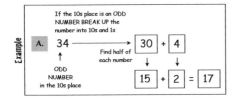

Example

A. If the 10s place is an ODD NUMBER BREAK UP the number into 10s and 1s

34 → Find half of each number → 30 + 4 → 15 + 2 = 17

ODD NUMBER in the 10s place

Cut the following numbers in half

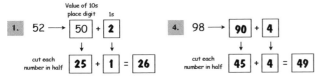

Value of 10s place digit | 1s

1. 52 → 50 + 2
cut each number in half → 25 + 1 = 26

4. 98 → 90 + 8
cut each number in half → 45 + 4 = 49

2. 38 → 30 + 8
cut each number in half → 15 + 4 = 19

5. 74 → 70 + 4
cut each number in half → 35 + 2 = 37

3. 76 → 70 + 6
cut each number in half → 35 + 3 = 38

6. 58 → 50 + 8
cut each number in half → 25 + 4 = 29

41

Halving Numbers when the 10s Digit is Odd

Cut the following numbers in half by breaking up the numbers into 10s and 1s

Value of 10s place digit | 1s

1. 34 → 30 + 4
cut each number in half → 15 + 2 = 17

6. 78 → 70 + 8
cut each number in half → 35 + 4 = 39

2. 72 → 70 + 2
cut each number in half → 35 + 1 = 36

7. 54 → 50 + 4
→ 25 + 2 = 27

3. 38 → 30 + 8
cut each number in half → 15 + 4 = 19

8. 96 → 90 + 6
→ 45 + 3 = 48

4. 92 → 90 + 2
cut each number in half → 45 + 1 = 46

9. 52 → 50 + 2
→ 25 + 1 = 26

5. 36 → 30 + 6
cut each number in half → 15 + 3 = 18

10. 74 → 70 + 4
→ 35 + 2 = 37

42

Halving Numbers with Odd Digits

Method #1: Breaking up the number into 100s, 10s and 1s

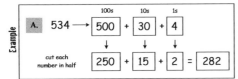

Example

A. 534 → 500 + 30 + 4
cut each number in half → 250 + 15 + 2 = 282

Cut the following numbers in half by breaking up the numbers into 100s, 10s and 1s

100s | 10s | 1s

1. 356 → 300 + 50 + 6
cut each number in half → 150 + 25 + 3
= 178

4. 586 → 500 + 80 + 6
cut each number in half → 250 + 40 + 3
= 293

2. 278 → 200 + 70 + 8
cut each number in half → 100 + 35 + 4
= 139

5. 372 → 300 + 70 + 2
cut each number in half → 150 + 35 + 1
= 186

3. 732 → 700 + 30 + 2
cut each number in half → 350 + 15 + 1
= 366

6. 958 → 900 + 50 + 8
cut each number in half → 450 + 25 + 4
= 479

43

Halving Numbers when the 10s Digit is Odd

The Subtract 1, Insert 1 Trick

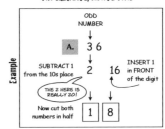

Example

A. ODD NUMBER

3 6

SUBTRACT 1 from the 10s place → 2 (THE 2 HERE IS REALLY 20!)

INSERT 1 in FRONT of the digit → 16

Now cut both numbers in half → 1 8

Cut the following numbers in half

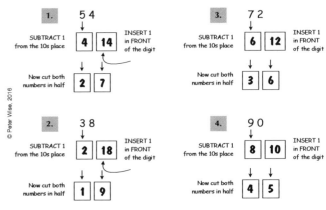

1. 5 4
SUBTRACT 1 from the 10s place → 4 | 14 ← INSERT 1 in FRONT of the digit
Now cut both numbers in half → 2 | 7

3. 7 2
SUBTRACT 1 from the 10s place → 6 | 12 ← INSERT 1 in FRONT of the digit
Now cut both numbers in half → 3 | 6

2. 3 8
SUBTRACT 1 from the 10s place → 2 | 18 ← INSERT 1 in FRONT of the digit
Now cut both numbers in half → 1 | 9

4. 9 0
SUBTRACT 1 from the 10s place → 8 | 10 ← INSERT 1 in FRONT of the digit
Now cut both numbers in half → 4 | 5

44

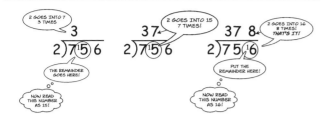

Intro to Short Division

2 GOES INTO 7 3 TIMES!

3
2)7⁽¹5⁾6

THE REMAINDER GOES HERE!

NOW READ THIS NUMBER AS 15!

2 GOES INTO 15 7 TIMES!

37
2)7⁽¹5⁾6

2 GOES INTO 16 8 TIMES! THAT'S IT!

378
2)75⁽¹6⁾

PUT THE REMAINDER HERE!

NOW READ THIS NUMBER AS 16!

Solve the following problems using SHORT DIVISION

Circles on the numbers are helpful for now, but you won't usually have them

1. 367
    2)7⁽¹3⁾⁽¹4⁾

2. 268
    2)5⁽¹3⁾⁽¹6⁾

3. 195
    2)3⁽¹9⁾⁽¹0⁾

4. 4696
    2)9⁽¹3⁾⁽¹9⁾⁽¹2⁾

5. 449
    2)8⁽¹9⁾⁽¹8⁾

NO REMAINDER, SO DON'T PUT ANYTHING IN THE CIRCLE!

6. 380
    2)7⁽¹6⁾0

7. 28967
    2)5⁽¹7⁾⁽¹9⁾⁽¹3⁾⁽¹4⁾

8. 41638
    2)8⁽¹3⁾⁽¹2⁾⁽¹7⁾⁽¹6⁾

© Peter Wise, 2016

45

Short Division Practice

Solve the following problems using SHORT DIVISION

1. 498
    2)9⁽¹8⁾⁽¹6⁾

2. 170
    2)3⁽¹4⁾0

3. 3517
    2)7⁽¹0⁾⁽¹3⁾⁽¹4⁾

4. 4053
    2)8⁽¹1⁾⁽¹0⁾6

5. 882
    2)1⁽¹7⁾⁽¹6⁾4

6. 297 ½ ← remainder
    2)5⁽¹9⁾⁽¹5⁾

7. 314 ½ ← remainder
    2)6⁽²9⁾

8. 4018 ½
    2)8⁽0⁾⁽³7⁾

9. 1500 ½
    2)3⁽¹0⁾⁽0⁾1

10. 4867 ½
    2)9⁽¹7⁾⁽¹3⁾⁽¹5⁾

© Peter Wise, 2016

46

Short Division Practice

Solve the following problems using SHORT DIVISION

1. 469
    2)9⁽¹3⁾⁽¹8⁾

2. 356
    2)7⁽¹1⁾⁽¹2⁾

3. 3017
    2)6⁽0⁾⁽³4⁾

4. 4053
    2)8⁽¹1⁾⁽¹0⁾6

5. 1798 ½ ← remainder
    2)3⁽¹5⁾⁽¹9⁾⁽¹7⁾

WHAT DO YOU NOTICE WHEN THE NUMBER 2 DIVIDES INTO ODD NUMBERS?

6. 261 ½ ← remainder
    2)5⁽¹2⁾3

7. 437 ½ ← remainder
    2)8⁽7⁾⁽¹5⁾

8. 3005 ½ ← remainder
    2)6⁽0⁾⁽¹1⁾⁽¹1⁾

9. 968 ½ ← remainder
    2)1⁽9⁾⁽¹3⁾⁽¹7⁾

10. 3929 ½ ← remainder
    2)7⁽¹8⁾⁽¹5⁾⁽¹9⁾

© Peter Wise, 2016

47

Short Division Practice

Solve the following problems using SHORT DIVISION

1. 260
    2)5⁽¹2⁾0

2. 417
    2)8⁽3⁾⁽¹4⁾

3. 2964
    2)5⁽¹9⁾⁽¹2⁾8

4. 4791
    2)9⁽¹5⁾⁽¹8⁾2

5. 1522 ½
    2)3⁽¹0⁾4⁽¹5⁾

6. 498 ½ ← remainder
    2)9⁽¹9⁾⁽¹7⁾

7. 180 ½
    2)3⁽¹6⁾1

8. 2369 ½
    2)4⁽¹7⁾⁽¹3⁾⁽¹9⁾

9. 1787 ½
    2)3⁽¹5⁾⁽¹7⁾⁽¹5⁾

10. 3591 ½
    2)7⁽¹1⁾⁽¹8⁾3

© Peter Wise, 2016

48

Short Division Practice

Page 49

Solve the following problems using SHORT DIVISION

1. $5\overline{)6\,^17\,^25}$ = 135

2. $5\overline{)8\,^31\,^15}$ = 163

3. $5\overline{)3\,^35\,^94\,^0}$ = 718

4. $5\overline{)7\,^20\,0\,^55}$ = 1401

5. $5\overline{)9\,^42\,^24\,^45}$ = 1849

6. $5\overline{)8\,^39\,^46}$ = 179 r $\frac{1}{5}$ ← remainder

7. $5\overline{)4\,^47\,^23}$ = 94 r $\frac{3}{5}$ ← remainder

8. $5\overline{)9\,^46\,^18\,^37}$ = 1937 r $\frac{2}{5}$ ← remainder

9. $5\overline{)6\,^12\,^28\,^33}$ = 1256 r $\frac{3}{5}$ ← remainder

10. $5\overline{)7\,^25\,^33\,^99}$ = 1507 r $\frac{4}{5}$ ← remainder

© Peter Wise, 2016

Page 50

Solve the following problems using SHORT DIVISION

1. $5\overline{)7\,^23\,^35}$ = 147

2. $5\overline{)9\,^42\,^25}$ = 185

3. $5\overline{)6\,^18\,^30\,^55}$ = 1361

4. $5\overline{)2\,2\,^26\,^10}$ = 452

5. $5\overline{)8\,^30\,1\,^15}$ = 1603

6. $5\overline{)5\,2\,^27}$ = 105 r $\frac{2}{5}$ ← remainder

7. $5\overline{)6\,^19\,^46}$ = 139 r $\frac{1}{5}$ ← remainder

8. $5\overline{)2\,8\,^37\,^21}$ = 574 r $\frac{1}{5}$ ← remainder

9. $5\overline{)8\,^37\,^29\,^42}$ = 1758 r $\frac{2}{5}$ ← remainder

10. $5\overline{)9\,^41\,^16\,^12}$ = 1832 r $\frac{2}{5}$ ← remainder

© Peter Wise, 2016

Page 51

Solve the following problems using SHORT DIVISION

1. $3\overline{)4\,^11\,^24}$ = 138

2. $4\overline{)5\,^17\,^16}$ = 144

3. $2\overline{)7\,^13\,^19\,^18}$ = 3699

4. $3\overline{)7\,^11\,^28}$ = 239 r $\frac{1}{3}$ ← remainder

5. $2\overline{)9\,^15\,^13\,^11}$ = 4765 r $\frac{1}{2}$ ← remainder

6. $5\overline{)8\,^34\,^43\,^39}$ = 1687 r $\frac{4}{5}$ ← remainder

7. $3\overline{)5\,^23\,^24\,7}$ = 1782 r $\frac{1}{3}$ ← remainder

8. $4\overline{)8\,0\,6\,^23}$ = 2015 r $\frac{3}{4}$ ← remainder

9. $5\overline{)9\,^41\,^14\,^48}$ = 1829 r $\frac{3}{5}$ ← remainder

10. $3\overline{)8\,^20\,^22\,^14}$ = 2674 r $\frac{2}{3}$ ← remainder

© Peter Wise, 2016

Page 52

52

Adding Nines

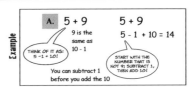

Example

A. $5 + 9$ $5 + 9$

THINK OF IT AS: 5 − 1 + 10!

9 is the same as 10 − 1

You can subtract 1 before you add the 10

$5 - 1 + 10 = 14$

START WITH THE NUMBER THAT IS NOT 9; SUBTRACT 1, THEN ADD 10!

Adding 9 is the same as "Subtract 1, add 10"

Add nines by SUBTRACTING 1 and ADDING 10

1. 8 + 9 → Start here → −1 = **7** + 10 = **17**

2. 6 + 9 → −1 = **5** + 10 = **15**

3. 4 + 9 → −1 = **3** + 10 = **13**

4. 7 + 9 → −1 = **6** + 10 = **16**

5. 3 + 9 → −1 = **2** + 10 = **12**

6. 12 + 9 → −1 = **11** + 10 = **21**

7. 27 + 9 → −1 = **26** + 10 = **36**

8. 14 + 9 → −1 = **13** + 10 = **23**

9. 36 + 9 → −1 = **35** + 10 = **45**

10. 75 + 9 → −1 = **74** + 10 = **84**

© Peter Wise, 2016

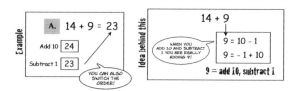

Adding Nines

Example

A. 14 + 9 = 23

Add 10 [24]

Subtract 1 [23]

YOU CAN ALSO SWITCH THE ORDER!

Idea behind this

14 + 9

WHEN YOU ADD 10 AND SUBTRACT 1 YOU ARE REALLY ADDING 9!

9 = 10 - 1
9 = - 1 + 10

9 = add 10, subtract 1

Solve the following addition problems by adding 10 and subtracting 1

1. 5 + 9
+10 [15]
-1 [14] ← answer

5. 27 + 9
+10 [37]
-1 [36]

9. 569 + 9
+10 [579]
-1 [578]

2. 13 + 9
+10 [23]
-1 [22] ← answer

6. 56 + 9
+10 [66]
-1 [65]

10. 842 + 9
+10 [852]
-1 [851]

3. 16 + 9
+10 [26]
-1 [25]

7. 38 + 9
+10 [48]
-1 [47]

11. 236 + 9
+10 [246]
-1 [245]

4. 38 + 9
+10 [48]
-1 [47]

8. 72 + 9
+10 [82]
-1 [81]

12. 6,775 + 9
+10 [6,785]
-1 [6,784]

53

Subtracting Nines

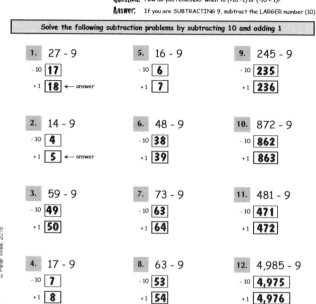

Example

A. 15 - 9 = 6

Subtract 10 [5]

Add 1 [6]

YOU CAN ALSO SWITCH THE ORDER!

Idea behind this

15 - 9

WHEN YOU SUBTRACT 10 AND ADD 1 YOU ARE REALLY SUBTRACTING 9!

-9 = - 10 + 1
-9 = + 1 - 10

-9 = subtract 10, add 1

Question: How do you remember when to (+10 -1) or (-10 + 1)?

Answer: If you are SUBTRACTING 9, subtract the LARGER number (10)

Solve the following subtraction problems by subtracting 10 and adding 1

1. 27 - 9
-10 [17]
+1 [18] ← answer

5. 16 - 9
-10 [6]
+1 [7]

9. 245 - 9
-10 [235]
+1 [236]

2. 14 - 9
-10 [4]
+1 [5] ← answer

6. 48 - 9
-10 [38]
+1 [39]

10. 872 - 9
-10 [862]
+1 [863]

3. 59 - 9
-10 [49]
+1 [50]

7. 73 - 9
-10 [63]
+1 [64]

11. 481 - 9
-10 [471]
+1 [472]

4. 17 - 9
-10 [7]
+1 [8]

8. 63 - 9
-10 [53]
+1 [54]

12. 4,985 - 9
-10 [4,975]
+1 [4,976]

54

Mixed Review

Cut the following numbers in half

1. 58 → [50] + [8]
   10s   1s
cut each number in half [25] + [4] = [29]

2. 94 → [90] + [4]
cut each number in half [45] + [2] = [47]

Cut the following numbers in half by breaking up the numbers into 100s, 10s and 1s

3. 738 → [700] + [30] + [8]
   100s   10s   1s
cut each number in half [350] + [15] + [4]
= [369]

4. 394 → [300] + [90] + [4]
cut each number in half [150] + [45] + [2]
= [197]

Add nines by SUBTRACTING 1 and ADDING 10

5. 7 + 9
↓
-1 = [6] + 10 = [16]

6. 24 + 9
↓
-1 = [23] + 10 = [33]

Solve the following subtraction problems by subtracting 10 and adding 1

7. 23 - 9
WHEN YOU SUBTRACT 9S, YOU SUBTRACT THE LARGER NUMBER (10).
-10 [13]
+1 [14] ← answer

8. 34 - 9
-10 [24]
+1 [25] ← answer

9. 462 - 9
-10 [452]
+1 [453] ← answer

55

Adding Eights

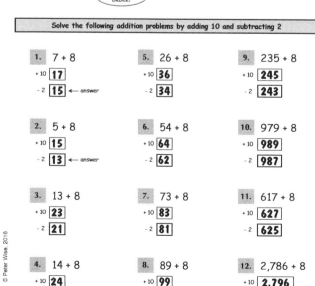

Example

A. 13 + 8 = 21

Add 10 [23]

Subtract 2 [21]

YOU CAN ALSO SWITCH THE ORDER!

Idea behind this

13 + 8

WHEN YOU SUBTRACT 2 AND ADD 10 YOU ARE REALLY ADDING 8!

8 = 10 - 2
8 = - 2 + 10

8 = add 10, subtract 2

Solve the following addition problems by adding 10 and subtracting 2

1. 7 + 8
+10 [17]
-2 [15] ← answer

5. 26 + 8
+10 [36]
-2 [34]

9. 235 + 8
+10 [245]
-2 [243]

2. 5 + 8
+10 [15]
-2 [13] ← answer

6. 54 + 8
+10 [64]
-2 [62]

10. 979 + 8
+10 [989]
-2 [987]

3. 13 + 8
+10 [23]
-2 [21]

7. 73 + 8
+10 [83]
-2 [81]

11. 617 + 8
+10 [627]
-2 [625]

4. 14 + 8
+10 [24]
-2 [22]

8. 89 + 8
+10 [99]
-2 [97]

12. 2,786 + 8
+10 [2,796]
-2 [2,794]

56

Subtracting Eights

Example

A. 17 - 8 = 9

Subtract 10 [7]

Add 2 [9]

YOU CAN ALSO SWITCH THE ORDER!

Idea behind this

17 - 8

WHEN YOU SUBTRACT 10 AND ADD 2 YOU ARE REALLY SUBTRACTING 8!

-8 = -10 + 2
-8 = +2 - 10

-8 = subtract 10, add 2

Solve the following subtraction problems by subtracting 10 and adding 2

1. 11 - 8
-10 [1]
+2 [3] ← answer

2. 13 - 8
-10 [3]
+2 [5] ← answer

3. 15 - 8
-10 [5]
+2 [7]

4. 14 - 8
-10 [4]
+2 [6]

5. 27 - 8
-10 [17]
+2 [19]

6. 25 - 8
-10 [15]
+2 [17]

7. 21 - 8
-10 [11]
+2 [13]

8. 32 - 8
-10 [22]
+2 [24]

9. 356 - 8
-10 [346]
+2 [348]

10. 261 - 8
-10 [251]
+2 [253]

11. 742 - 8
-10 [732]
+2 [734]

12. 9,857 - 8
-10 [9,847]
+2 [9,849]

© Peter Wise, 2016

57

Adding Eighteens

Example

A. 17 + 18 = 21

Add 20 [37]

Subtract 2 [35]

YOU CAN ALSO SWITCH THE ORDER!

Idea behind this

another way to think of 18

TO ADD 18 JUST ADD 20 AND THEN SUBTRACT 2!

18 = 20 - 2
18 = - 2 + 20

add 20, subtract 2

Pattern: UP a 20, DOWN 2

Solve the following addition problems by adding 20 and subtracting 2

1. 3 + 18
+20 [23]
-2 [21] ← answer

2. 7 + 18
+20 [27]
-2 [25] ← answer

3. 14 + 18
+20 [34]
-2 [32]

4. 36 + 18
+20 [56]
-2 [54]

5. 59 + 18
+20 [79]
-2 [77]

6. 27 + 18
+20 [47]
-2 [45]

7. 63 + 18
+20 [83]
-2 [81]

8. 97 + 18
+20 [117]
-2 [115]

9. 469 + 18
+20 [479]
-2 [477]

10. 139 + 18
+20 [159]
-2 [157]

11. 827 + 18
+20 [847]
-2 [845]

12. 3,684 + 18
+20 [3,704]
-2 [3,702]

© Peter Wise, 2016

58

+ 19 = Up a 20, Down a One

Example

A. 47 + 19 =   47 + 20 = [ ] - 1 = [ ]
(20 - 1)

+ 19 IS REALLY "UP TWO TENS, DOWN A ONE!!"   same as + 19!

Solve these + 19 problems by adding 20, then subtracting 1

1. 26 + 19 = [46] - 1 = [45]   now your answer is the same as if you had added 19 in the first place!
add 26 + 20

2. 77 + 19 = [97] - 1 = [96]
add 77 + 20

3. 41 + 19 = [61] - 1 = [60]
+ 20

4. 83 + 19 = [103] - 1 = [102]

5. 59 + 19 = [79] - 1 = [78]

6. 16 + 19 = [36] - 1 = [35]

7. 79 + 19 = [98]
add 20 and then subtract 1

8. 28 + 19 = [47]

9. 35 + 19 = [54]

10. 62 + 19 = [81]

11. 74 + 19 = [93]

© Peter Wise, 2016

59

Adding Nineteens

Example

A. 35 + 19 = 54

Add 20 [55]

Subtract 1 [54]

YOU CAN ALSO SWITCH THE ORDER!

Idea behind this

another way to think of 19

TO ADD 19 JUST ADD 20 AND THEN SUBTRACT 1!

19 = 20 - 1
19 = - 1 + 20

add 20, subtract 1

Solve the following addition problems by adding 20 and subtracting 1

1. 7 + 19
+20 [27]
-1 [26] ← answer

2. 3 + 19
+20 [23]
-1 [22] ← answer

3. 58 + 19
+20 [78]
-1 [77]

4. 16 + 19
+20 [36]
-1 [35]

5. 49 + 19
+20 [69]
-1 [68]

6. 75 + 19
+20 [95]
-1 [94]

7. 82 + 19
+20 [102]
-1 [101]

8. 127 + 19
+20 [147]
-1 [146]

9. 324 + 19
+20 [344]
-1 [343]

10. 563 + 19
+20 [583]
-1 [582]

11. 795 + 19
+20 [815]
-1 [814]

12. 2,386 + 19
+20 [2,406]
-1 [2,405]

© Peter Wise, 2016

60

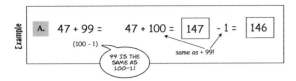

+ 99 = Up a 100, Down a One

Example

A. 47 + 99 =   47 + 100 = **147** - 1 = **146**

(100 - 1)

same as + 99!

99 IS THE SAME AS 100–1!

Solve these + 99 problems by adding 100, then subtracting 1

1. 37 + 99 = **137** - 1 = **136**   now your answer is the same as if you had added 99 in the first place!
   + 100

2. 62 + 99 = **162** - 1 = **161**   7. 6148 + 99 = **6247**
   + 100

3. 735 + 99 = **835** - 1 = **834**   8. 3875 + 99 = **3974**
   + 100

4. 316 + 99 = **416** - 1 = **415**   9. 99 + 1763 = **1862**

5. 99 + 643 = **743** - 1 = **742**   10. 99 + 8210 = **8309**

WHAT IS 50 – 1?

6. 99 + 824 = **924** - 1 = **923**   11. 5650 + 99 = **5749**

© Peter Wise, 2016

61

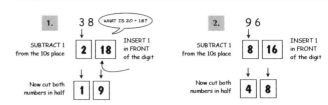

Mixed Review

Cut the following numbers in half, using the "Minus 1, Insert 1" Trick

1. 3 8   *WHAT IS 20 + 18?*
   SUBTRACT 1 from the 10s place **2** **18**   INSERT 1 in FRONT of the digit
   Now cut both numbers in half **1** **9**

2. 9 6
   SUBTRACT 1 from the 10s place **8** **16**   INSERT 1 in FRONT of the digit
   Now cut both numbers in half **4** **8**

ONE MORE FOR THE FIVES: Find the sums of the following numbers

10 add the 5s   **10** add the 5s

3. 15 + 35 = **50**   4. 45 + 25 = **70**

40 add the tens place   **60** add the tens place

Solve the following addition problems by adding 10 and subtracting 2

5. 5 + 8   6. 27 + 8   7. 354 + 8
   + 10 **15**   + 10 **37**   + 10 **364**
   - 2 **13** ← answer - 2 **35**   - 2 **362**

Solve the following addition problems by adding 20 and subtracting 1

8. 6 + 19   9. 38 + 19   10. 627 + 19
   + 20 **26**   + 20 **58**   + 20 **647**
   - 1 **25** ← answer - 1 **57**   - 1 **646**

© Peter Wise, 2016

62

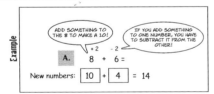

+/- Same Amounts Trick

Example

ADD SOMETHING TO THE 8 TO MAKE A 10!   *IF YOU ADD SOMETHING TO ONE NUMBER, YOU HAVE TO SUBTRACT IT FROM THE OTHER!*

A.   +2 -2
     8 + 6 =

New numbers: **10** + **4** = 14

Add to the first number to round up, then subtract from the other number

1. +**2** -**2**
    8 + 5 =
New numbers: **10** + **3** = **13**

HOW MUCH DO YOU NEED TO ADD TO MAKE 20?

2. +**1** -**1**
    9 + 8 =
    10 + **7** = **17**

3. +**2** -**2**
    8 + 7 =
    10 + **5** = **15**

4. +**3** -**3**
    7 + 9 =
    10 + **6** = **16**

HOW MUCH DO YOU NEED TO MAKE 90?

5. +**4** -**4**
    86 + 6 =
    90 + **2** = **92**

6. +**2** -**2**
    18 + 6 =
    20 + **4** = **24**

7. +**3** -**3**
    17 + 7 =
    20 + **4** = **24**

8. +**4** -**4**
    16 + 9 =
    20 + **5** = **25**

9. +**1** -**1**
    19 + 7 =
    20 + **6** = **26**

10. +**1** -**1**
    119 + 8 =
    120 + **7** = **127**

© Peter Wise, 2016

63

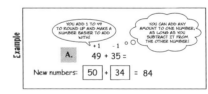

+/- Same Amounts Trick

Example

YOU ADD 1 TO 49 TO ROUND UP AND MAKE A NUMBER EASIER TO ADD WITH!   *YOU CAN ADD ANY AMOUNT TO ONE NUMBER, AS LONG AS YOU SUBTRACT IT FROM THE OTHER NUMBER!*

A.   +1 -1
     49 + 35 =

New numbers: **50** + **34** = 84

Add to the first number to round up, then subtract from the other number

1. +**1** -**1**
    39 + 26 =
New numbers: **40** + **25** = **65**

WHAT DO YOU ADD TO MAKE THIS A ROUND NUMBER?

2. +**2** -**2**
    58 + 35 =
    60 + **33** = **93**

3. +**1** -**1**
    89 + 27 =
    90 + **26** = **116**

4. +**3** -**3**
    17 + 45 =
    20 + **42** = **62**

5. +**1** -**1**
    119 + 54 =
    120 + **53** = **173**

6. +**2** -**2**
    38 + 13 =
    40 + **11** = **51**

7. +**4** -**4**
    56 + 35 =
    60 + **31** = **91**

8. +**2** -**2**
    18 + 68 =
    20 + **66** = **86**

9. +**3** -**3**
    57 + 24 =
    60 + **21** = **81**

10. +**2** -**2**
    128 + 47 =
    130 + **45** = **175**

© Peter Wise, 2016

64

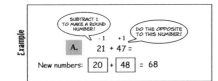

+/- Same Amounts Trick (page 65)

Example

SUBTRACT 1 TO MAKE A ROUND NUMBER!   DO THE OPPOSITE TO THIS NUMBER!

$$-1 \quad +1$$
A. 21 + 47 =

New numbers: 20 + 48 = 68

Subtract from the first number to round down, then add to the other number

1. $-1 \quad +1$
51 + 35 =
New numbers: 50 + 36 = 86

6. $-2 \quad +2$
22 + 35 =
(WHAT CAN YOU SUBTRACT TO MAKE THIS AN EASY ROUND NUMBER?)
20 + 37 = 57

2. $-1 \quad +1$
11 + 84 =
10 + 85 = 95

7. $-2 \quad +2$
12 + 84 =
10 + 86 = 96

or
$-1 \quad +1$

8. $-2 \quad +2$
52 + 29 =
50 + 31 = 81

3. $-1 \quad +1$
71 + 18 =
70 + 19 = 89

4. $-1 \quad +1$
61 + 38 =
60 + 39 = 99

9. $-2 \quad +2$
22 + 76 =
20 + 78 = 98

5. $-1 \quad +1$
121 + 53 =
120 + 54 = 174

10. $-2 \quad +2$
132 + 57 =
130 + 59 = 189

65

+/- Same Amounts Trick (page 66)

Add or subtract in the boxes, then solve these problems mentally

1. $+1 \quad -1$
19 + 17 = **36**

7. $-2 \quad +2$
42 + 35 = **77**

2. $-1 \quad +1$
31 + 64 = **95**

8. $+3 \quad -3$
27 + 45 = **72**

3. $+1 \quad -1$
49 + 13 = **62**

9. $-2 \quad +2$
52 + 39 = **91**

4. $-1 \quad +1$
61 + 38 = **99**

10. $+3 \quad -3$
37 + 26 = **63**

5. $-1 \quad +1$
121 + 73 = **194**

11. $-2 \quad +2$
132 + 57 = **189**

6. $+2 \quad -2$
258 + 23 = **281**

12. $+2 \quad -2$
118 + 17 = **135**

66

Mixed Review (page 67)

Calculate the tens and the ones; then add them together

1. 7 tens and 56 = **126**
2. 12 tens and 23 = **143**
3. 9 tens and 25 = **115**
4. 14 tens and 57 = **197**

Make 20s and tell how much over 20

5. 17 + 9
17 + 3 + 6 = **26**
= 20

6. 16 + 8
16 + 4 + 4 = **24**
= 20

Make 50s by finding the missing numbers

7. 1 4
   + 3 **6**
   ─────
    5 0

8. 2 7
   + 2 **3**
   ─────
    5 0

9. 3 2
   + **18**
   ─────
    5 0

10. 3 9
    + **11**
    ─────
     5 0

Add to the first number to round up, then subtract from the other number

11. $+3 \quad -3$
7 + 5 =
New numbers: 10 + 2 = 12

12. $+2 \quad -2$
18 + 6 =
20 + 4 = 24

13. $+1 \quad -1$
29 + 8 =
30 + 7 = 37

Solve these + 18 problems by adding 20, then subtracting 2

14. 53 + 18 = **73** - 2 = **71**
53 + 20

15. 76 + 18 = **96** - 2 = **94**
76 + 20

67

Subtracting in Steps (page 68)

A. 100 - 35 = 65
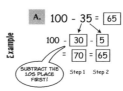

You don't have to subtract numbers all at once!

You can break up subtraction problems into smaller subtraction problems

100 - 30 - 5
= 70 = 65

(SUBTRACT THE 10S PLACE FIRST!) Step 1   Step 2

Solve the following subtraction problems by subtracting in steps

1. 100 - 73
100 - 70 - 3 = **27**

6. 48 - 25
48 - 20 - 5 = **23**

2. 100 - 46
100 - 40 - 6 = **54**

7. 70 - 38
70 - 30 - 8 = **32**

3. 80 - 19
80 - 10 - 9 = **61**

8. 200 - 54
200 - 50 - 4 = **146**

4. 160 - 32
160 - 30 - 2 = **128**

9. 457 - 25
457 - 20 - 5 = **432**

5. 180 - 45
180 - 40 - 5 = **135**

10. 875 - 252
875 - 200 - 50 - 2 = **623**

68

© Peter Wise, 2016

Calculate Mentally

Calculate mentally

11. 5 + 2 + **3** = 10
13. 12 + 2 + **6** = 20
12. 2 + 6 + **2** = 10
14. 3 + 13 + **4** = 20

Calculate mentally

15. 50 - 8 = **42**
17. 80 - 4 = **76**
16. 50 - 18 = **32**
18. 70 - 21 = **49**

Add or subtract the following numbers mentally; line them up correctly in your head!

1. 648 + 310 = **958**
6. 7965 - 500 = **7465**
2. 362 + 136 = **498**
7. 320 + 60 + 17 = **397**
3. 2475 - 300 = **2175**
8. 7965 - 500 = **7465**
4. 3000 - 300 + 20 = **2720**
9. 1000 - 420 = **580**
5. 482 - 50 = **432**
10. 1000 - 321 = **679**

69

Subtracting, Using a Between Number

A. 25 - 17   #1 Reverse the order   17   25

#2 Pick an easy number between the two numbers. (Usually it is best to start with the lower number and go up to the nearest ten.)

Find a middle number
Add the differences between it   17 **20** 25
                                          3   5

#3 Find the difference between the middle number and the lower and higher numbers

#4 Add these numbers—you're done!   **3 + 5 = 8**
                                      the answer!
                                    25 - 17 = 8

Example

Find a between number and add the differences

1. 22 - 16   16 **20** 22 ← Reverse the order
   Take the lower number, go up to the nearest 10 put this in the middle box

   Number in the middle minus 16 → **4**   **2** ← 22 minus the number in the middle

   Add the two numbers above → **6**
   This is the answer to 22 - 16

2. 23 - 14   14 **20** 23 ← Reverse the order
   Take the lower number, go up to the nearest 10 put this in the middle box

   Number in the middle minus the lower number → **6**   **3** ← Higher number minus the number in the middle

   Add the two numbers above → **9**
   This is the answer to 23 - 14

70

Subtracting, Using a Between Number

Find a between number and add the differences

1. 21 - 13   13 **20** 21 ← Reverse the order
   Take the lower number, go up to the nearest 10 put this in the middle box

   Number in the middle minus 13 → **7**   **1** ← 21 minus the number in the middle

   Add the two numbers above → **8**
   This is the answer to 21 - 13

2. 28 - 11   **11** **20** **28** ← Reverse the order
   Take the lower number, go up to the nearest 10 put this in the middle box

   Find the difference → **9**   **8** ← Find the difference

   Add the two numbers above → **17**
   ↑ Answer

3. 34 - 16   **16** **20** **34** ← Reverse the order
   Take the lower number, go up to the nearest 10 put this in the middle box

   Find the difference → **4**   **14** ← Find the difference

   Add the two numbers above → **18**
   ↑ Answer

4. 43 - 18   **18** **20** **43** ← Reverse the order

   → **2**   **23** ←

   Add the two numbers above → **25**
   ↑ Answer

71

Subtracting, Using a Between Number

Find a between number and add the differences

1. 23 - 17   Between number ↓
   17 **20** **23** ← Reverse the order
   Take the lower number, go up to the nearest 10 put this in the middle box

   Find the difference → **3**   **3** ← Find the difference

   Add → **6**

2. 27 - 18   Between number
   18 **20** **27** ← Reverse the order

   Find the difference → **2**   **7** ← Find the difference

   Add → **9**

3. 35 - 19   Between number
   19 **20** **35**

   Find the difference → **1**   **15** ← Find the difference

   Add → **16**

4. 42 - 27   Between number
   27 **30** **42**

   3   **12**

   Add → **15**

72

Subtracting, Using a Between Number

Find a between number and add the differences

1. 62 - 23

Between number ↓
| 23 | 30 | 62 | ← Reverse the order

Find the difference → | 7 | | 32 | ← Find the difference

Add → | 39 |

2. 73 - 45

Between number ↓
| 45 | 50 | 73 |

Find the difference → | 5 | | 23 | ← Find the difference

Add → | 28 |

3. 58 - 23

Between number ↓
| 23 | 30 | 58 |

Find the difference → | 7 | | 28 | ← Find the difference

Add → | 35 |

4. 74 - 36

Between number ↓
| 36 | 40 | 74 |

| 4 | | 34 |

Add → | 38 |

© Peter Wise, 2016

73

Subtracting, Using Amounts Above & Below 100

Use the number 100 as the between number and add the differences

1. 108 - 94

How far is 108 from 100? How far is 94 from 100?
| 8 | | 6 |

Add the two differences: | 14 |

2. 120 - 98

How far is 120 from 100? How far is 98 from 100?
| 20 | | 2 |

Add | 22 |

3. 115 - 88

How far from 100? How far from 100?
| 15 | | 12 |

Add | 27 |

4. 133 - 89

How far from 100? How far from 100?
| 33 | | 11 |

Add | 44 |

5. 141 - 73

How far from 100? How far from 100?
| 41 | | 27 |

Add | 68 |

6. 125 - 84

How far from 100? How far from 100?
| 25 | | 16 |

Add | 31 |

7. 129 - 80

How far from 100? How far from 100?
| 29 | | 20 |

Add | 49 |

8. 124 - 88

How far from 100? How far from 100?
| 24 | | 12 |

Add | 36 |

© Peter Wise, 2016

74

Subtracting, Using Amounts Above & Below 100

Use the number 100 as the between number and add the differences MENTALLY

1. 106 - 97

How much above 100? How much below 100?

Add the two differences: | 9 |

2. 108 - 92

How much above 100? How much below 100?

Add the two differences: | 16 |

3. 110 - 89

How much above 100? How much below 100?

Add the two differences: | 21 |

4. 125 - 80

How much above 100? How much below 100?

Add the two differences: | 45 |

5. 112 - 60

How much above 100? How much below 100?

Add the two differences: | 52 |

6. 115 - 93

How much above 100? How much below 100?

Add the two differences: | 22 |

7. 120 - 88

How much above 100? How much below 100?

Add the two differences: | 32 |

8. 150 - 75

How much above 100? How much below 100?

Add the two differences: | 75 |

9. 180 - 85

How much above 100? How much below 100?

Add the two differences: | 95 |

10. 135 - 75

How much above 100? How much below 100?

Add the two differences: | 60 |

© Peter Wise, 2016

75

The DM-10 Trick

D – DIVIDE
M – MULTIPLY
10 – WITH TEN OR POWERS OF TEN (100'S, 1000S, 10THS, 100THS, ETC..)

IF YOU MULTIPLY OR DIVIDE A NUMBER BY A POWER OF 10, YOU JUST SLIDE THE DECIMAL ON THE ORIGINAL NUMBER!

D (DIVIDE) | **M (MULTIPLY)**

When you divide by 10s you slide to the LEFT | When you multiply by 10s you slide to the RIGHT

THIS IS WHY THE "D" COMES FIRST IN "DM-10"!

LET'S START BY DIVIDING BY 10S

WHEN YOU DIVIDE, YOU SLIDE TO THE LEFT!

Examples

A. 3.67 ÷ 10 = | .367 |

ONE ZERO, ONE SLIDE!

B. .42 ÷ 10 = | .042 |

IF YOU NEED TO, ADD ONE OR MORE ZEROS TO GIVE ROOM TO SLIDE

(YOU CAN'T SLIDE IN BLANK SPACE!)

1. 37 ÷ 10 = | 3.7 |

REMEMBER! THERE IS AN INVISIBLE DECIMAL POINT HERE!

2. 9.2 ÷ 10 = | .92 |

3. .8 ÷ 10 = | .08 |

4. 456 ÷ 10 = | 45.6 |

5. 800 ÷ 10 = | 80 |

6. 63.2 ÷ 10 = | 6.32 |

7. 800 ÷ 100 = | 8 |

TWO ZEROS, TWO SLIDES!

8. 751 ÷ 1,000 = | .751 |

STILL TO THE LEFT BECAUSE WE ARE DIVIDING!

HOW MANY SLIDES DO YOU THINK WITH THREE ZEROS?

9. 913.7 ÷ 1,000 = | .9137 |

TIP: IT HELPS TO DRAW ARROWS FOR EACH SLIDE!

© Peter Wise, 2016

76

Page 77

D (DIVIDE) — When you divide by 10s you slide to the LEFT

M (MULTIPLY) — When you multiply by 10s you slide to the RIGHT

LET'S START BY MULTIPLYING BY 10S

WHEN YOU MULTIPLY, YOU SLIDE TO THE RIGHT!

Examples

A. $4.23 \times 10 = 42.3$

ONE ZERO, ONE SLIDE!

B. $12 \times 10 = 120$

other ways of writing 12: $12.$ 12.0

1. $.62 \cdot 10 = 6.2$

2. $.357 \cdot 100 = 35.7$

3. $.78 \cdot 100 = 78$

4. $.7 \cdot 100 = 70$

5. $80 \cdot 10 = 800$

6. $.09 \cdot 10 = .9$

7. $.09 \cdot 100 = 9$

8. $.0053 \cdot 100 = .53$

9. $.06 \cdot 1{,}000 = 60$

10. $4.38 \cdot 1{,}000 = 4380$

11. $59.3 \cdot 100 = 5930$

12. $364.2 \cdot 100 = 36{,}420$

© Peter Wise, 2016

Page 78

D (DIVIDE) — When you divide by 10s you slide to the LEFT

M (MULTIPLY) — When you multiply by 10s you slide to the RIGHT

1. $350 \cdot 10 = 3500$

2. $350 \div 10 = 35$

3. $350 \div 100 = 3.5$

4. $.79 \cdot 10 = 7.9$

5. $4.26 \cdot 10 = 42.6$

6. $.06 \cdot 100 = 6$

7. $.75 \cdot 100 = 75$

8. $6.3 \cdot 10 = 63$

9. $6.3 \cdot 100 = 630$

10. $2.7 \cdot 1000 = 2700$

11. $.1 \cdot 10 = 1$

12. $.01 \cdot 100 = 1$

13. $36 \div 10 = 3.6$

14. $.004 \cdot 100 = .4$

15. $.004 \cdot 1000 = 4$

16. $382 \div 100 = 3.82$

17. $7 \div 10 = .7$

18. $95 \div 1000 = .095$

19. $7.6 \cdot 100 = 760$

20. $.49 \div 10 = .049$

© Peter Wise, 2016

Page 79

D (DIVIDE) — When you divide by 10s you slide to the LEFT

M (MULTIPLY) — When you multiply by 10s you slide to the RIGHT

Count the zeros and slide!

1. $4 \cdot 100 = 400$

2. $3 \div 10 = .3$

3. $17 \div 100 = .17$

4. $6 \div 100 = .06$

5. $3.6 \cdot 10 = 36$

6. $3.6 \cdot 100 = 360$

7. $.07 \cdot 100 = 7$

8. $.08 \cdot 1000 = 80$

9. $45 \div 10 = 4.5$

10. $6.03 \cdot 100 = 603$

11. $27 \div 1000 = .027$

12. $5 \div 1000 = .005$

13. $.078 \cdot 1000 = 78$

14. $.78 \cdot 1000 = 780$

15. $4.6 \cdot 1000 = 4600$

16. $.27 \div 100 = .0027$

Review Problems

17. $3 + 37 = 40$

18. $6 + 74 = 80$

19. $12 + 18 = 30$

20. $11 + 39 = 50$

21. $14 + 16 = 30$

22. $18 + 82 = 100$

© Peter Wise, 2016

Page 80

Powers of Ten

1. Skip count by 20s

   20 **40 60 80 100 120 140 160 180 200**

2. Skip count by 30s

   30 **60 90 120 150 180 210 240 270 300**

POWERS OF 10!

Examples

A.
- 10 as a factor 1 time: $10^1 = 10$ → 10
- 10 as a factor 2 times: $10^2 = 100$ (1 and TWO zeros) → $10 \cdot 10$
- 10 as a factor 3 times: $10^3 = 1000$ (1 and THREE zeros) → $10 \cdot 10 \cdot 10$

ANY NUMBER (EXCEPT 0) TO THE ZERO POWER = ONE!

B. $10^0 = 1$ (1 and no zeros) — NOT zero!

1. $10^4 = 10{,}000$

2. $10^2 = 100$

3. $10^3 = 1000$

4. $10^1 = 10$

5. $10^0 = 1$

6. $4 \cdot 10^2 = 400$

7. $.314 \cdot 10^2 = 31.4$

8. $.018 \cdot 10^4 = 180$

9. $.27 \cdot 10^3 = 270$

Write the correct exponents

10. $100 = 10^2$

11. $10 = 10^1$

12. $1000 = 10^3$

13. $100{,}000 = 10^5$

14. $10{,}000 = 10^4$

15. $1 \text{ million} = 10^6$

Multiply by powers of 10

16. $7 \cdot 10^2 = 700$

17. $72 \cdot 10^3 = 72{,}000$

18. $16 \cdot 10^0 = 16$

© Peter Wise, 2016

Multiplying by Multiples of Ten

When multiplying by 10, just add one zero onto the number, when multiplying by 100 add two zeros, when multiplying by 1000 add three zeros!

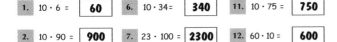

Example

A. $10 \cdot 3 = 30$ 1 zero   1 zero   JUST ADD ONE ZERO ONTO THE THREE!

B. $100 \cdot 3 = 300$ 2 zeros   2 zeros

Multiply by 10 or multiples of 10 (just add on the right number of zeros!)

1. $10 \cdot 6 =$ **60**	**6.** $10 \cdot 34 =$ **340**	**11.** $10 \cdot 75 =$ **750**
2. $10 \cdot 90 =$ **900**	**7.** $23 \cdot 100 =$ **2300**	**12.** $60 \cdot 10 =$ **600**
3. $6 \cdot 10 =$ **60**	**8.** $4 \cdot 1000 =$ **4000**	**13.** $100 \cdot 21 =$ **2100**
4. $100 \cdot 7 =$ **700**	**9.** $16 \cdot 1000 =$ **16,000**	**14.** $28 \cdot 1000 =$ **28,000**
5. $10 \cdot 100 =$ **1000**	**10.** $100 \cdot 5 =$ **500**	**15.** $10 \cdot 640 =$ **6400**

Add or subtract mentally

16. $2560 + 233 =$ **2793**	**19.** $5472 + 308 =$ **5780**
17. $7350 + 2406 =$ **9756**	**20.** $9765 - 314 =$ **9451**
18. $4685 - 253 =$ **4432**	**21.** $5000 - 265 =$ **4735**

© Peter Wise, 2016

81

Multiplying by Multiples of Ten

Multiply the non-zero numbers first; then add on the number of zeros in the problem

1. $30 \cdot 20 =$ **600**	**11.** $60 \cdot 900 =$ **54,000**
2. $40 \cdot 600 =$ **24,000**	**12.** $110 \cdot 300 =$ **33,000**
3. $70 \cdot 3 =$ **210**	**13.** $30 \cdot 30 =$ **900**
4. $30 \cdot 90 =$ **2700**	**14.** $800 \cdot 800 =$ **640,000**
5. $80 \cdot 400 =$ **32,000**	**15.** $120 \cdot 30 =$ **3600**
6. $20 \cdot 1200 =$ **24,000**	**16.** $70 \cdot 40 =$ **2800**
7. $500 \cdot 700 =$ **350,000**	**17.** $250 \cdot 200 =$ **50,000**
8. $600 \cdot 70 =$ **42,000**	**18.** $70 \cdot 900 =$ **63,000**
9. $90 \cdot 500 =$ **45,000**	**19.** $20 \cdot 1700 =$ **34,000**
10. $8 \cdot 6000 =$ **48,000**	**20.** $200 \cdot 420 =$ **84,000**

© Peter Wise, 2016

82

Division with Zeros

$2\cancel{0}\overline{)4\cancel{0}} = 2)\overline{4} = \boxed{2}$ Same as the fraction $\frac{4\cancel{0}}{2\cancel{0}} = \frac{4}{2} = \boxed{2}$

DIVIDING BOTH SIDES BY 10!

Cancel the zeros from both sides and solve the following division problems

1. $2\cancel{00}\overline{)4\cancel{00}}$ = $\boxed{2}$ Same as the fraction $\frac{400}{200}$ YOU CAN CANCEL THE SAME WAY WITH FRACTIONS!

HERE YOU CANCEL TWO ZEROS FROM BOTH SIDES!

2. $3\cancel{0}\overline{)15\cancel{0}}$ = $\boxed{5}$

3. $6\cancel{00}\overline{)12\cancel{00}}$ = $\boxed{2}$

4. $6\cancel{00}\overline{)120,000}$ = $\boxed{200}$

5. $7\cancel{000}\overline{)420,000}$ = $\boxed{60}$

6. $8\cancel{00}\overline{)24,000}$ = $\boxed{30}$

7. $5\cancel{0}\overline{)25\cancel{0}}$ = $\boxed{5}$

8. $9\cancel{0}\overline{)270\cancel{0}}$ = $\boxed{300}$

9. $8\cancel{0}\overline{)720\cancel{0}}$ = $\boxed{90}$

10. $51\cancel{0}\overline{)510\cancel{0}}$ = $\boxed{10}$

11. $12\cancel{0}\overline{)480\cancel{0}}$ = $\boxed{40}$

12. $8\cancel{0}\overline{)16,00\cancel{0}}$ = $\boxed{200}$

13. $4\cancel{000}\overline{)28,000}$ = $\boxed{7}$

© Peter Wise, 2016

83

Mixed Review

Use the DM-10 Trick to multiply or divide the following numbers

1. $61 \div 10 =$ **6.1**	**4.** $3.14 \div 100 =$ **.0314**
2. $7 \div 100 =$ **.07**	**5.** $.017 \div 10 =$ **.0017**
3. $2.5 \times 100 =$ **250**	**6.** $.005 \times 100 =$ **.5**

Cancel the zeros from both sides and solve the following division problems

7. $4\cancel{0}\overline{)280\cancel{0}}$ = $\boxed{70}$ **8.** $8\cancel{00}\overline{)320\cancel{0}}$ = $\boxed{4}$ **9.** $7\cancel{000}\overline{)350,000}$ = $\boxed{50}$

Double the following numbers by going LEFT to RIGHT

10. $37 + 37 =$

will you have a carry? (y) n

add the TENS place
add 1 more for a carry $\rightarrow$ **7** **4**

add the ONES place
LAST digit only

11. $29 + 29 =$

will you have a carry? (y) n

add the TENS place
add 1 more for a carry $\rightarrow$ **5** **8**

add the ONES place
LAST digit only

Cut the following numbers in half by breaking up the numbers into 10s and 1s

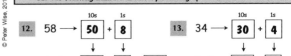

12. $58 \rightarrow$ **50** (10s) + **8** (1s)

cut each number in half $\rightarrow$ **25** + **4** = **29**

13. $34 \rightarrow$ **30** (10s) + **4** (1s)

cut each number in half $\rightarrow$ **15** + **2** = **17**

© Peter Wise, 2016

84

Mixed Review

Use the DM-10 Trick to multiply or divide the following numbers

1. $4.2 \times 10 =$ **42**

3. $.073 \times 1000 =$ **73**

2. $3.14 \times 1000 =$ **3140**

4. $765 \div 100 =$ **7.65**

Add to the first number to round up, then subtract from the other number

5. $+\boxed{1}$ $-\boxed{1}$
$29 + 43 =$
New numbers: $\boxed{30} + \boxed{42} = \boxed{72}$

or -1 $+1$
7. $+\boxed{3}$ $-\boxed{3}$
$+1$ $57 + 39 =$
New numbers: $\boxed{60} + \boxed{36} = \boxed{96}$

6. $+\boxed{2}$ $-\boxed{2}$
$38 + 27 =$
New numbers: $\boxed{40} + \boxed{25} = \boxed{65}$

8. $+\boxed{1}$ $-\boxed{1}$
$39 + 25 =$
New numbers: $\boxed{40} + \boxed{24} = \boxed{64}$

Solve the following subtraction problems by subtracting in twice

9. $100 - 46$
$100 - \boxed{40} - \boxed{6} = \boxed{54}$

11. $70 - 24$
$70 - \boxed{20} - \boxed{4} = \boxed{46}$

10. $100 - 37$
$100 - \boxed{30} - \boxed{7} = \boxed{63}$

12. $54 - 26$
$54 - \boxed{20} - \boxed{6} = \boxed{28}$

85

Calculate Mentally

Add the following numbers mentally; line them up correctly in your head!

1. $420 + 30 + 8 =$ **458**

2. $3600 + 200 + 7 =$ **3807**

3. $670 + 19 =$ **689**

4. $5400 + 300 + 26 =$ **5726**

5. $30 + 200 + 45$
$=$ **275**

6. $7900 + 400$
$=$ **8300**

7. $680 + 25$
$=$ **705**

Calculating with Tens

8. 8 tens and 3 $=$ **83**

10. $.012 \cdot 10 =$ **.12**

12. $7 + \boxed{13} = 20$

9. 8 tens and 23 $=$ **103**

11. $473 \div 100 =$ **4.73**

13. $12 + \boxed{18} = 30$

Division with Tens

14. $400 \overline{)1200}$ → **3**

15. $60 \overline{)5400}$ → **90**

16. $800 \overline{)560000}$ → **700**

Put into "Standard Notation" (regular numbers)

17. $70 + 800 + 6 + .3 + .02 =$ **876.32**

86

The Triangle Trick

NUMBERS CAN BE WRITTEN AS SINGLE DIGITS FOLLOWED BY ZEROS. THE DIGITS AND ZEROS CAN BE MADE TO FORM A TRIANGLE.

This is called "Expanded Notation"

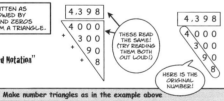

4,398
4000
+ 300
+ 90
+ 8

THESE READ THE SAME! (TRY READING THEM BOTH OUT LOUD!)

4,398
4000
300
90
8

HERE IS THE ORIGINAL NUMBER!

Make number triangles as in the example above

1. 7,621
$\boxed{7000}$
$+ \boxed{600}$
$+ \boxed{20}$
$+ \boxed{1}$

3. 9,035
$\boxed{9000}$
$+ \boxed{000}$
$+ \boxed{30}$
$+ \boxed{5}$

2. 53,842
$\boxed{50000}$
$+ \boxed{3000}$
$+ \boxed{800}$
$+ \boxed{40}$
$+ \boxed{2}$

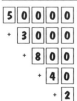

4. 67,089
$\boxed{60000}$
$+ \boxed{7000}$
$+ \boxed{000}$
$+ \boxed{80}$
$+ \boxed{9}$

87

Expanded Notation With Powers of 10

YOU CAN EXPRESS EACH DIGIT OF A NUMBER AS A POWER OF 10!

THIS IS ANOTHER WAY TO WRITE EXPANDED NOTATION!

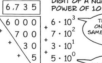

6,735
6000
+ 700
+ 30
+ 5

$6 \cdot 10^3$
$7 \cdot 10^2$
$3 \cdot 10^1$
$5 \cdot 10^0$

THE EXPONENT ON THE 10 IS THE SAME AS THE NUMBER OF ZEROS!

ANY NUMBER TO THE ZERO POWER = 1!

...EXCEPT ZERO!

Make number triangles as in the example above

TIMES 10^3 10^2 10^1 10^0

1. 7,628
$\boxed{7000} = \boxed{7} \cdot 10^{\boxed{3}}$
$+ \boxed{600} = \boxed{6} \cdot 10^{\boxed{2}}$
$+ \boxed{20} = \boxed{2} \cdot 10^{\boxed{1}}$
$+ \boxed{8} = \boxed{8} \cdot 10$

3. 5,314
$\boxed{5} \cdot 10^{\boxed{3}}$
$+ \boxed{3} \cdot 10^{\boxed{2}}$
$+ \boxed{1} \cdot 10^{\boxed{1}}$
$+ \boxed{4} \cdot 10^{\boxed{0}}$

2. 49,237
$\boxed{40000} = \boxed{4} \cdot 10^{\boxed{4}}$
$+ \boxed{9000} = \boxed{9} \cdot 10^{\boxed{3}}$
$+ \boxed{200} = \boxed{2} \cdot 10^{\boxed{2}}$
$+ \boxed{30} = \boxed{3} \cdot 10^{\boxed{1}}$
$+ \boxed{7} = \boxed{7} \cdot 10^{\boxed{0}}$

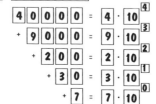

4. 87,462
$\boxed{8} \cdot 10^{\boxed{4}}$
$+ \boxed{6} \cdot 10^{\boxed{3}}$
$+ \boxed{4} \cdot 10^{\boxed{2}}$
$+ \boxed{6} \cdot 10^{\boxed{1}}$
$+ \boxed{2} \cdot 10^{\boxed{0}}$

88

Mixed Review

Fill in the number triangles

1. | 5 , 2 8 3 |

| 5 | 0 | 0 | 0 |
+ | 2 | 0 | 0 |
+ | 8 | 0 |
+ | 3 |

3. | 8 , 0 9 7 |

| 8 | 0 | 0 | 0 |
+ | 0 | 0 | 0 |
+ | 9 | 0 |
+ | 7 |

Fill in the number triangle using powers of 10

2. | 2 3 , 1 6 4 |

| 2 | 0 | 0 | 0 | 0 | = | 2 | · 10^4
+ | 3 | 0 | 0 | 0 | = | 3 | · 10^3
+ | 1 | 0 | 0 | = | 1 | · 10^2
+ | 6 | 0 | = | 6 | · 10^1
+ | 4 | = | 4 | · 10^0

Add the following numbers mentally; line them up correctly in your head!

3. 250 + 20 + 6 = **276**

5. 640 + 30 + 15 = **685**

4. 9 + 320 + 30 = **359**

6. 270 + 40 + 16 = **326**

Intro to Rounding

Example

A. Round 26 to the 10s place

#1 Circle the correct place

#2 Look to the number to the RIGHT

#3 If the digit to the RIGHT is 5 or more, add one more! to the CIRCLED number!

#4 4 or less, the circled number stays the SAME

#5 Add zeros to the RIGHT of the circled number

10s place; circle it

②6

②6

The next door number is more than 5, so add one to the circled number

③0 — After you know the circled number add a zero to the RIGHT of this!

Round the following numbers to the 10s place

Remember to circle the 10s place digit & draw an arrow to the right

IF THIS NUMBER IS 5 OR MORE, THEN YOU ADD 1 TO THE CIRCLED NUMBER!

1. ③7 rounded to the 10s place = | 4 | 0 |

CIRCLE THE 10S PLACE DIGIT!

ROUND NUMBERS NEED TO HAVE 1 OR MORE ZEROS AFTER THEM!

UNLESS THEY ARE DECIMALS!

2. ④9 rounded to the 10s place is | 5 | 0 |

IS THE 4 ENOUGH TO BUMP UP THE CIRCLED NUMBER?

4. ①8 rounded to the 10s place is | 2 | 0 |

3. ⑦4 rounded to the 10s place is | 7 | 0 |

5. ⑥2 rounded to the 10s place is | 6 | 0 |

Rounding to the 10's Place

Round the following numbers to the 10s place

Circle the 10s place digit and draw an arrow to the right

1. ③6 rounded to the 10s place is | 4 | 0 |

2. ②5 | 3 | 0 |

3. ⑨8 | 1 | 0 | 0 |

4. ⑥4 | 6 | 0 |

5. ⑥5 | 7 | 0 |

6. ⑧6 | 9 | 0 |

7. ①3 | 1 | 0 |

8. ⑤5 | 6 | 0 |

9. ②7 | 3 | 0 |

10. ⑨2 | 9 | 0 |

11. ⑧8 | 9 | 0 |

12. ①5 | 2 | 0 |

Rounding to the 10's Place: 3-Digit Numbers

A. Round 6 3 9 to the 10s place

#1 Round the 10s place digit normally

#2 COPY the digit to the LEFT of the circle number

#3 Put a ZERO to the RIGHT of the circle number

HOW TO FIND THE 10'S PLACE:

6 3 9   5 2 3 3
↑ 10s   ↑ 10s

Write or imagine a 10 lined up on the RIGHT side

The 1 on the ten points up to the 10s place!

Example

6③9 rounded to the 10s place is

COPY the numbers on this side ← → Zeros on this side

6④0

Round the following numbers to the 10s place

Circle the 10s place digit and draw an arrow to the right

1. 7⑤8 rounded to the 10s place is | 7 | 6 | 0 |

2. 2①6 rounded to the 10s place is | 2 | 2 | 0 |

3. 4⑦4 rounded to the 10s place is | 4 | 8 | 0 |

4. 1④5 | 1 | 5 | 0 |

5. 4④4 | 4 | 4 | 0 |

6. 5⑤5 | 5 | 6 | 0 |

7. 2⑦6 | 2 | 8 | 0 |

8. 3⓪5 | 3 | 1 | 0 |

9. 9①4 | 9 | 1 | 0 |

Rounding with Carrying

You will only carry if the circle number is 9

A. Example

The 9 raises up to a 10, so you carry 1

4⑨6 rounded to the 10s place is

→ Zeros on this side

5⓪0

You can also think of it as 49 + 1 = 50

Round the following numbers to the 10s place (not all problems have a carry)

Remember to circle the 10s place digit and draw an arrow to the right

1. 2⑨8 rounded to the 10s place is
   3 0 0

   WHAT HAPPENS IF YOU ADD 1 TO 9?

2. 8⑨7 rounded to the 10s place is
   0 0 0

3. 1⑨4
   1 9 0

4. 5⑨5
   6 0 0

5. 8⓪5
   8 1 0

6. 8⓪4
   8 0 0

7. 3④4
   3 4 0

8. 5⑨6
   6 0 0

9. ⑨5
   1 0 0

10. 7⑧9
    7 9 0

11. 7⑨8
    8 0 0

12. 4①3
    4 1 0

13. 7②7
    7 3 0

14. 9⑨5
    1 0 0 0

93

Rounding 4-Digit Numbers

A. If you round to the 10s place

2 3⑦6 rounded to the 10s place:

COPY on this side ← → ZEROS on this side

2 3⑧0

B. If you round to the 100s place

2③7 6 rounded to the 100s place:

COPY on this side ← → ZEROS on this side

2④0 0

Round the following numbers to the proper place

Remember to circle the digit in the correct place and draw an arrow to the right

1. 1 2⑧6 rounded to the 10s place is
   1 2 9 0

2. 1②8 6 rounded to the 100s place is
   1 3 0 0

3. 5 8⑦3 rounded to the 10s place is
   5 8 7 0

4. 5⑧7 3 rounded to the 100s place is
   5 9 0 0

5. 4 1⑨6 rounded to the 10s place is
   4 2 0 0

6. 3 0⓪7 rounded to the 10s place is
   3 0 1 0

7. 3⓪0 7 rounded to the 100s place is
   3 0 0 0

8. 2⑨7 1 rounded to the 100s place is
   3 0 0 0

9. 6 1⑨8 rounded to the 10s place is
   6 2 0 0

10. 2 3⑦5 rounded to the 10s place is
    2 3 8 0

94

Rounding to the Ones Place

Look next door

A. Round 3⑦.8 2 to the 1s place = [3 8]

or 3 8.0 0

You don't need these decimals

#1 Circle the ONEs place

#2 If the digit next door is 5 or more add 1 to the circled number

#3 COPY the digits to the LEFT of the circle number

#4 You don't need any decimals numbers or even the decimal point if you're rounding to the ones place!

Round the following numbers to the ones place

Don't forget the circles & arrows

1. ⑧.6 rounded to the 1s place is
   9

2. ②.6 7
   3

3. 4⑤.3
   45

4. 7⑧.5 1
   79

5. 4 3⑤.7 9
   436

6. 6①.8 2 7
   62

7. 2 9⓪.6 0 2
   291

8. 1⑤.0 9
   15

95

Rounding to the Tenths Place

A. Round 2 3.①6 to the 10ths place = [2 3.2]

#1 Round the 10s place digit normally

#2 COPY the digit to the LEFT of the circle number

#3 Put a ZERO to the RIGHT of the circle number

#4 You can ignore the zeros to the right of the rounded tenths place

HOW TO FIND THE TENTHS PLACE:

2 3.1 6
↑ ↑
10ths

With decimals numbers, the 1 points to the decimal and you have a zero for every decimal

10 has one zero
There is one zero for each decimal place

Round the following numbers to the tenths place; remember the circles & arrows

1. 3.⑥5
   3.7

2. 1 5.⑧6
   15.9

3. 9.1⑦2
   9.17

4. 5 6.⓪9
   56.1

5. 1 0.①2
   10.1

6. 2 4.⓪4
   24.0

7. 3 7.⑤5
   37.6

8. 9 0 5.④6
   905.5

9. 1 8.⑥7 2
   18.7

10. 6.⓪0 9
    6.0

11. 8 2.⑤0 8
    82.5

12. 2.④9 9
    2.5

96

Mixed Review

Round the following numbers to the 10s place

1. 7̂5 → **8** 0

3. 5̂4 → **5** **0**

5. 4̂3 → **4** **0**

2. 2̂6 → **3** 0

4. 3̂9 → **4** **0**

6. 6̂6 → **7** **0**

Round the following 3-digit numbers to the TENS place

7. 3 7̂ 2 rounded to the TENS place is 3 **7** 0

9. 3 0̂ 7 → **3** **1** **0**

11. 2 5̂ 5 → **2** **6** **0**

8. 4 2̂ 8 rounded to the 10s place is **4** **3** 0

10. 5 8̂ 2 → **5** **8** **0**

12. 6 2̂ 5 → **6** **3** **0**

Find the sum

12. 9 tens and 37 = **127**

13. 16 tens and 26 = **186**

Add the original numbers, add the additional tens, solve the new problems

14. 9 + 8 = **17**   29 + 28
how much more is this? **40**
29 + 28 = **57**

15. 17 + 6 = **23**   47 + 26
how much more is this? **50**
47 + 26 = **73**

© Peter Wise, 2016

97

Mixed Review

Calculate the tens and the ones; then add them together

1. 4 tens and 17 = **57**

3. 14 tens and 25 = **165**

2. 8 tens and 23 = **103**

4. 15 tens and 42 = **192**

Double the following numbers

5. 23 → **46**

7. 37 → **74**

9. 239 → **478**

6. 19 → **38**

8. 48 → **96**

10. 366 → **732**

Cut the following numbers in half by breaking up the numbers into 10s and 1s

11. 78 → **70** + **8**
cut each number in half **35** + **4** = **39**

12. 34 → **30** + **4**
15 + **2** = **17**

Round the following numbers to the ONES place

13. 5 . 4 rounded to the 1s place is **5**

14. 7 2 . 6 4 → **73**

15. 3 1 5 . 4 5 → **315**

Round the following numbers to the TENTHS place

16. 6 . 3 5 → **6.4**

17. 3 . 5 4 → **3.5**

18. 1 3 . 7 5 4 → **13.8**

© Peter Wise, 2016

98

What Does the Mean Mean?

A. Find the mean of 3 and 7:

$(3 + 7) \div 2 = \boxed{10}$ or $\dfrac{(3 + 7)}{2} = \boxed{10}$

DIVIDE BY 2 BECAUSE YOU ADDED 2 NUMBERS!

Add the numbers and divide by the # of numbers you added!

Find the mean (average) of the following numbers

1. 2 and 6
$(\boxed{2} + \boxed{6}) \div \boxed{2} = \boxed{4}$
add first   then divide

6. 5 and 9
$(\boxed{14}) \div \boxed{2} = \boxed{7}$

2. 5 and 7
$(\boxed{5} + \boxed{7}) \div \boxed{2} = \boxed{6}$
add first   then divide

7. 8 and 8
$(\boxed{16}) \div \boxed{2} = \boxed{8}$

3. 2 and 10
$(\boxed{2} + \boxed{10}) \div \boxed{2} = \boxed{6}$
add first   then divide

8. 13 and 7
$(\boxed{20}) \div \boxed{2} = \boxed{10}$
13 IS 3 ABOVE THIS
7 IS 3 BELOW THIS!

4. 3 and 15
$(\boxed{18}) \div \boxed{2} = \boxed{9}$

9. 25 and 5
$(\boxed{30}) \div \boxed{2} = \boxed{15}$

5. 4 and 20
$(\boxed{24}) \div \boxed{2} = \boxed{12}$

10. 10 and 32
$(\boxed{42}) \div \boxed{2} = \boxed{21}$

© Peter Wise, 2016

99

What Does the Mean Mean?

The Mean (aka "average") is the middle between two numbers; "equal piles"

Draw a point for each of the numbers and for the mean

You find the mean by adding the numbers and dividing by the number of addends

1. 3 and 5
$(\boxed{8}) \div \boxed{2} = \boxed{4}$
add 3 + 5   then divide by 2 (because you added two numbers)

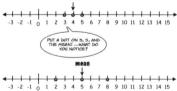
PUT A DOT ON 3, 5, AND THE MEAN! ...WHAT DO YOU NOTICE?

2. 2 and 8
$(\boxed{10}) \div \boxed{2} = \boxed{5}$

3. 1 and 11
$(\boxed{12}) \div \boxed{2} = \boxed{6}$

4. 10 and 14
$(\boxed{24}) \div \boxed{2} = \boxed{12}$

THE MEAN (AVERAGE) LEVELS ALL OF THE NUMBERS

5. 4 + 6 = **10**   What is the mean of 4 and 6? $(\boxed{10}) \div \boxed{2} = \boxed{5}$
$\boxed{5} + \boxed{5} = \boxed{10}$ (same as 4 + 6)
mean + mean

6. 3 + 11 = **14**   What is the mean of 3 and 11? $(\boxed{14}) \div \boxed{2} = \boxed{7}$
$\boxed{7} + \boxed{7} = \boxed{14}$ (same as 3 + 11)
mean + mean

© Peter Wise, 2016

100

Mean Practice

Find the mean (average) of the following numbers

ADD THE MULTIPLES OF 5 FIRST!

1. 3, 7, and 8 ← 3 numbers

   $(3 + 7 + 8) \div 3 = 6$

   add first   *then divide*

2. 10, 6, and 8

   $(10 + 6 + 8) \div 3 = 8$

   add first   *then divide*

3. 40, 20, 30

   $90 \div 3 = 30$

   sum of the 3 numbers

4. 2, 5, and 8

   $15 \div 3 = 5$

   REMEMBER TO DIVIDE BY THE NUMBER OF ADDENDS IN THE PROBLEM!

5. 10, 10, 2, and 6

   $28 \div 4 = 7$

6. 4, 2 and 6

   $12 \div 3 = 4$

7. 4, 20, and 6

   $30 \div 3 = 10$

8. 2, 15, 10, 5, and 3

   $35 \div 5 = 7$

   WHICH PAIRS OF NUMBERS WOULD BE BEST TO ADD FIRST?

9. 9, 7, 1, and 3

   $20 \div 4 = 5$

10. 15, 10, 5, 18

    $48 \div 4 = 12$

11. 10, 12, 8, and 2

    $32 \div 4 = 8$

12. 50, 10, 5, and 15

    $80 \div 4 = 20$

13. 2, 3, 10, 3, and 7

    $25 \div 5 = 5$

14. 12, 6, 1, 2, and 9

    $30 \div 5 = 6$

© Peter Wise, 2016

101

Mean Practice

Find the mean (average) of the following numbers

1. 2, 4, 2, 4

   $(12) \div 4 = 3$

2. 6, 12, 3

   $21 \div 7 = 3$

3. 13, 9, 2

   $24 \div 3 = 8$

4. 8, 3, 12, 1

   $24 \div 4 = 6$

5. 3, 11, 6, 3, 2

   $25 \div 5 = 5$

6. 6, 20, 8, 10

   $44 \div 4 = 11$

7. 20, 15, 25, 30, 10

   $100 \div 5 = 20$

8. 5, 5, 25, 5

   $40 \div 4 = 10$

9. 70, 70, 10

   $150 \div 3 = 50$

10. 5, 10, 30

    $45 \div 3 = 15$

11. 20, 40, 15

    $75 \div 3 = 25$

12. 5, 10, 15, 30

    $60 \div 4 = 15$

13. 7, 8, 8, 7, 5

    $35 \div 5 = 7$

    WHICH 2 PAIRS OF NUMBERS WOULD BE BEST TO ADD FIRST?

14. 24, 15, 30, 11

    $80 \div 4 = 20$

© Peter Wise, 2016

102

Mean Practice

Find the mean (average) of the following numbers

1. 10, 20, 18

   $48 \div 3 = 16$

2. 24, 40

   $64 \div 2 = 32$

3. 3, 11, 7

   $21 \div 3 = 7$

4. 10, 10, 19

   $39 \div 3 = 13$

5. 16, 18

   $34 \div 2 = 17$

6. 30, 50, 20, 20

   LOOK FOR THREE NUMBERS THAT ADD UP TO 100!

   $120 \div 4 = 30$

   START BY LOOKING AT THREE 10'S PLACE DIGITS THAT ADD UP TO 10!

7. 50, 70, 60

   $180 \div 3 = 60$

8. 13, 17, 10, 12, 18

   $70 \div 5 = 14$

9. 10, 14, 6, 8, 8, 8

   $54 \div 6 = 9$

10. 18, 12, 6

    $36 \div 3 = 12$

11. 6, 12, 7, 7

    $32 \div 4 = 8$

12. 30, 24

    $54 \div 2 = 27$

13. 100, 50, 60

    $210 \div 3 = 70$

14. 50, 25, 25, 200, 150

    $450 \div 5 = 90$

© Peter Wise, 2016

103

Intro to the Median

How do you find the Median?

Example

A.   12, 8, 3, 13, 7

   #1   Line the numbers up in order: 3, 7, 8, 12, 13

   #2   Find the middle number; this is the MEDIAN

   #3   With longer strings of numbers it can help to cross off the smallest number, greatest number, next smallest, etc. When you get to the middle, you have found the MEDIAN

     4, 4, 5, 8, 10, 10, 13, 14, 18, 18, 19, 25, 30

   #4   What if there are two middle numbers? Then you find the MEAN of the two middle numbers. This will be the MEDIAN!   3, 8, 10, 18

YOU CAN TELL THAT THE NUMBER BETWEEN 8 AND 10 IS 9 (THE MEAN)!

Use the MEAN of the two MIDDLE NUMBERS

Find the MEDIAN of the following numbers

1. 10, 9, 5, 4, 14

   4, 5, 9, 10, 14   Median = 9

   put them in order

2. 7, 11, 2, 7, 10

   TREAT DOUBLE NUMBERS JUST LIKE REGULAR NUMBERS!

   2, 7, 7, 10, 11   Median = 7

   put them in order

3. 3, 2, 11, 6, 10, 4

   2, 3, 4, 6, 10, 11   Median = 5

4. 9, 15, 8, 3, 25, 14, 21   Median = 14

   3, 8, 9, 14, 15, 21, 25

5. 20, 10, 5, 6, 12, 5   Median = 8

   5, 5, 6, 10, 12, 20

6. 12, 19, 5, 15, 2, 6   Median = 9

   2, 5, 6, 12, 15, 19

© Peter Wise, 2016

104

Mean, Median, Mode

Find the MEAN, MEDIAN, and MODE of the following numbers

Mode = number that occurs the most

Median = middle number

Mean = add the numbers, divide by the number of addends

1. 1, 3, 26
   Mean: **10**

2. 2, 7, 8
   Median: **7**

3. 14, 5, 8, 14
   Mode: **14**

4. 4, 4, 12, 30, 50
   Median: **12**

5. 30, 50, 10
   Mean: **30**

6. 7, 25, 6, 6
   Mode: **6**

7. 2, 8, 10, 12
   Median: **9**

8. 1, 8, 9
   Mean: **6**

9. 2, 6, 29, 6, 30
   Mode: **6**

10. 3, 5, 7
    Median **5**

11. 3, 12, 14, 18
    Median **13**

12. 1, 3, 5, 15
    Median **4**

13. 4, 4, 10, 2, 5
    Mean: **5**

14. 3, 4, 11
    Mean: **6**

15. 3, 7, 9, 10
    Median: **8**

16. 20, 40, 60
    Mean: **120**

17. 2, 11, 13, 16
    Median: **12**

THE *MODE* IS THE NUMBER THAT OCCURS THE *MOST*!

THIS NUMBER OCCURS THE *"MODST"* OFTEN!

© Peter Wise, 2016

105

Mean, Median, Mode

Find the MEAN, MEDIAN, and MODE of the following numbers

Mode = number that occurs the most

Median = middle number

Mean = add the numbers, divide by the number of addends

1. 2, 3, 5, 9
   Median: **4**

2. 5, 16, 16, 18
   Mode: **16**

3. 3, 6, 12
   Mean: **7**

4. 2, 6, 12, 13, 14
   Median: **12**

5. 2, 8, 14, 14
   Mode: **14**

6. 24, 27, 31
   Median: **27**

7. 3, 8, 11, 14, 16
   Median: **11**

8. 14, 3, 15, 16, 14
   Mode: **14**

9. 3, 17, 4
   Mean: **8**

10. 14, 15, 17, 19
    Median **16**

11. 1, 20, 6
    Mean: **9**

12. 8, 2, 5, 8, 7
    Mode: **8**

13. 3, 16, 18, 20
    Median: **17**

14. 2, 11, 2
    Mean: **5**

15. 9, 12, 21, 9, 25
    Mode: **9**

16. 15, 10, 5
    Mean: **10**

17. 4, 7, 9, 10
    Median: **8**

© Peter Wise, 2016

106

Mean, Median, Mode

Find the MEAN, MEDIAN, and MODE of the following numbers

1. 18, 6, 3
   Mean: **9**

2. 14, 1, 3
   Median **3**

3. 3, 5, 6, 10, 16
   Median: **6**

4. 2, 5, 7, 12, 18
   Median: **7**

5. 4, 18, 2
   Mean: **8**

6. 3, 5, 3, 8, 11
   Mode: **3**

7. 2, 4, 6, 7
   Median: **5**

8. 14, 27, 14, 39
   Mode: **14**

9. 2, 18, 7
   Mean: **9**

10. 3, 7, 3, 9
    Mode: **3**

11. 1, 5, 7, 12
    Median **6**

12. 14, 20, 2
    Mean: **12**

13. 4, 7, 8
    Median **7**

14. 4, 5, 5, 9
    Mode **5**

15. 20, 8, 5
    Mean **11**

16. 30, 80, 80, 20
    Mode **80**

© Peter Wise, 2016

107

Multiplying by Fives

Explanation

5 is half of 10

When you multiply by 5 it's the same as

(× 10) and (÷ 2)
OR
(÷ 2) and (× 10)

Cut the number in half (divide by 2)

Multiply by 10 (add on a zero)

Example

Cut in half; add a zero trick

12 × 5

Divide by 2 → 6

Add on a zero **60**

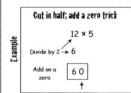

Multiply by 5 by dividing by 2 and then adding a zero at the end

1. 8 × 5 =
   Half of 8 (8 ÷ 2) **4 0** Add on a zero

2. 6 × 5 =
   Half of 6 (divide by 2) **3 0** Add on a zero

3. 14 × 5 =
   Half of 14 **7 0** Add on a zero

4. 18 × 5 =
   Divide by 2 **9 0** Add on a zero

5. 24 × 5 =
   Divide by 2 **12 0** Add on a zero

6. 28 × 5 =
   14 0 Add on a zero

7. 60 × 5 =
   300 Add on a zero

8. 32 × 5 =
   160

9. 44 × 5 =
   220 Add on a zero

10. 48 × 5 =
    240 Add on a zero

© Peter Wise, 2016

108

Multiplying by Fives

Multiply by 5 by dividing by 2 and then adding a zero at the end

1. 34 × 5 =
Half of 34 **17 0** Add on a zero

2. 38 × 5 =
Half of 38 **19 0** Add on a zero

3. 42 × 5 =
210 Add on a zero

4. 64 × 5 =
320

5. 36 × 5 =
180

6. 52 × 5 =
260

7. 54 × 5 =
270

8. 58 × 5 =
290

9. 66 × 5 =
330

10. 26 × 5 =
130

11. 78 × 5 =
390

12. 86 × 5 =
430

13. 76 × 5 =
380

14. 98 × 5 =
490

Multiplying by Fives

Multiply by 5 by dividing by 2 and then adding a zero at the end

1. 5 × 2 6 8 =
1 3 4 0
Half of 2   Half of 6   Half of 8   Add on a zero

2. 5 × 6 4 2 =
3 2 1 0
Half of 6   Half of 4   Half of 2   Add on a zero

3. 5 × 8 0 4 6 =
4 0 2 3 0
half of 8   0   4   6

4. 5 × 1 0 6 4 =
5 3 2 0
half of 10   64   Add on a zero

5. 5 × 3 6 3 8 =
1 8 1 9 0
half of   36   38

6. 5 × 3 4 1 6 =
1 7 0 8 0
half of   34   16

7. 5 × 5 2 1 4 =
2 6 0 7 0
half of   52   14

8. 5 × 8 6 5 4 =
4 3 2 7 0
54

9. 5 × 5 0 6 8 =
2 5 3 4 0

10. 5 × 7 0 5 6 =
3 5 2 8 0

Multiplying by Fives

Multiply by 5 by dividing by 2 and then sliding the decimal point one time to the RIGHT

Sliding the decimal point one time to the right is the same as multiplying by 10

1. 4 8 . 2 6 × 5 =
2 4 1 . 3
half of   4   8   2   6
slide the decimal one time to the RIGHT (same as multiplying by 10)

2. 6 . 2 4 8 × 5 =
3 1 . 2 4
...BECAUSE THE WAY WE'RE MULTIPLYING BY 5 IS "DIVIDE BY 2; TIMES 10!"

3. 8 0 . 5 4 × 5 =
4 0 2 . 7
half of   80   54
WHAT NUMBER DOUBLED EQUALS 54?

4. 2 6 . 5 2 × 5 =
1 3 2 . 6
half of   26   52

5. 3 . 6 8 4 × 5 =
1 8 . 4 2

6. 3 . 8 0 6 × 5 =
1 9 . 0 3

7. 3 0 3 . 2 × 5 =
1 5 1 . 6
30   32

8. 5 . 2 1 8 × 5 =
2 6 . 0 9
52   18

9. . 5 6 2 4 × 5 =
2 . 8 1 2
56

10. 7 2 . 5 8 × 5 =
3 6 2 . 9

Multiplying Odd Numbers by 5's

Any ODD number times 5 ends in FIVE

Example

7 × 5 =

#1 Subtract 1 from the 7 → **6**   (7 - 1 = 6)

#2 Divide by 2, but now add on a 5 → **3 5**

Multiply by 5 by dividing by 2 and then adding on a five at the end

1. 3 × 5
Subtract 1 from the 3 **2**
Divide by 2, add on a 5 **15**

2. 9 × 5
Subtract 1 from the 9 **2**
Divide by 2, add on a 5 **15**

3. 13 × 5
Subtract 1 from the 13 **12**
Divide by 2, add on a 5 **65**

4. 15 × 5
Subtract 1 from the 15 **14**
Divide by 2, add on a 5 **75**

5. 31 × 5
Subtract 1 from the 31 **30**
Divide by 2, add on a 5 **155**

6. 37 × 5
Subtract 1 from the 37 **36**
Divide by 2, add on a 5 **185**

7. 43 × 5
Subtract 1 from the 43 **42**
Divide by 2, add on a 5 **215**

8. 87 × 5
Subtract 1 from the 87 **86**
Divide by 2, add on a 5 **435**

9. 59 × 5
Subtract 1 from the 59 **58**
Divide by 2, add on a 5 **295**

Multiplying Odd Numbers by 5's

Multiply by 5 by dividing by 2 and adding on a 5

1. 17×5
Subtract 1 from the 17 → **16**
Divide by 2, add on a 5 → **85**

5. 23×5
Subtract 1 from the 23 → **22**
Divide by 2, add on a 5 → **115**

9. 33×5
Subtract 1 from the 33 → **32**
Divide by 2, add on a 5 → **165**

2. 43×5
Subtract 1 → **42**
Divide by 2, add on a 5 → **215**

6. 19×5
Subtract 1 → **18**
Divide by 2, add on a 5 → **95**

10. 27×5
Subtract 1 → **26**
Divide by 2, add on a 5 → **135**

3. 37×5
Subtract 1 → **36**
Divide by 2, add on a 5 → **185**

7. 53×5
Subtract 1 → **52**
Divide by 2, add on a 5 → **265**

11. 65×5
Subtract 1 → **64**
Divide by 2, add on a 5 → **325**

4. 21×5
Subtract 1 → **20**
Divide by 2, add on a 5 → **105**

8. 67×5
Subtract 1 → **66**
Divide by 2, add on a 5 → **335**

12. 77×5
Subtract 1 → **76**
Divide by 2, add on a 5 → **385**

© Peter Wise, 2016

104

113

Multiplying When Adding

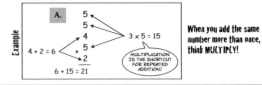

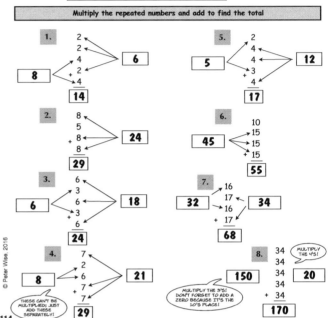

Example

A.
$$5$$
$$5$$
$$4$$
$$5$$
$$+ \ 2$$
$4 + 2 = 6$
$3 \times 5 = 15$
$6 + 15 = 21$

MULTIPLICATION IS THE SHORTCUT FOR REPEATED ADDITION!

When you add the same number more than once, think MULTIPLY!

Multiply the repeated numbers and add to find the total

1. **8**
2, 2, 4, 2, + 4 → **6**
14

5. **5**
2, 4, 4, 3, + 4 → **12**
17

2.
8, 5, + 8, 8 → **24**
29

6. **45**
10, 15, 15, 15 → **55**

3. **6**
6, 3, 6, 3, + 6 → **18**
24

7. **32**
16, 17, 16, + 17 → **34**
68

4. **8**
7, 2, 6, 7, + 7 → **21**
29

THESE CAN'T BE MULTIPLIED; JUST ADD THESE SEPARATELY!

8.
34, 34, 34, 34, + 34 → **150**, **20**
170

MULTIPLY THE 4'S!

MULTIPLY THE 3'S! DON'T FORGET TO ADD A ZERO BECAUSE IT'S THE 10'S PLACE!

© Peter Wise, 2016

114

Sum and Product

Find the SUM and the PRODUCT of the following numbers

SUM = answer to an ADDITION problem; PRODUCT = answer to a MULTIPLICATION problem

#			sum	product	#			sum	product
1.	7	3	10	21	13.	5	8	13	40
2.	5	4	9	20	14.	2	12	14	24
3.	6	2	8	12	15.	3	11	14	33
4.	3	8	11	24	16.	3	12	15	36
5.	9	3	12	27	17.	8	8	16	64
6.	3	4	7	12	18.	9	7	16	63
7.	8	7	15	56	19.	6	9	15	54
8.	2	9	11	18	20.	5	12	17	60
9.	6	4	10	24	21.	8	9	17	72
10.	7	5	12	35	22.	12	4	16	48
11.	8	6	14	48	23.	7	12	19	84
12.	4	9	13	36	24.	25	3	28	75

© Peter Wise, 2016

115

Difference and Quotient

Find the DIFFERENCE and the QUOTIENT of the following numbers

DIFFERENCE = answer to a SUBTRACTION problem; QUOTIENT = answer to a DIVISION problem

#			difference	quotient	#			difference	quotient
1.	8	2	6	4	13.	25	5	20	5
2.	15	5	10	3	14.	28	4	24	7
3.	12	3	9	4	15.	12	4	8	3
4.	16	2	14	8	16.	35	7	28	5
5.	18	3	15	6	17.	32	8	24	4
6.	20	5	15	4	18.	48	8	40	6
7.	70	10	60	7	19.	24	8	16	3
8.	24	6	18	4	20.	54	6	48	9
9.	14	2	12	7	21.	64	8	56	8
10.	16	4	12	4	22.	63	9	54	7
11.	24	2	22	12	23.	56	8	48	7
12.	30	6	24	5	24.	84	7	77	12

© Peter Wise, 2016

116

4 Operations with Numbers

			sum	product	difference	quotient
A.	6	2	8	12	4	3

Perform all four operations with the given numbers

			sum	product	difference	quotient
1.	10	2	12	20	8	5
2.	10	5	15	50	5	2
3.	9	3	12	27	6	3
4.	5	1	6	5	4	5
5.	12	3	15	36	9	4
6.	8	4	12	32	4	2
7.	15	3	18	45	12	5
8.	12	4	16	48	8	3
9.	20	2	22	40	18	10
10.	50	2	52	100	48	25

117

4 Operations with Numbers

Perform all four operations with the given numbers

			sum	product	difference	quotient
1.	20	5	25	100	15	4
2.	60	2	62	120	58	30
3.	100	10	110	1000	90	10
4.	20	4	24	80	16	5
5.	50	10	60	500	40	5
6.	30	2	32	60	28	15
7.	100	4	104	400	96	25
8.	40	20	60	800	20	2
9.	6	3	9	18	3	2
10.	24	2	26	48	22	12
11.	80	40	120	3200	40	2
12.	16	2	18	32	14	8

118

Finding New Factor Pairs

Use just these factors to make different multiplication problems

1. $3 \cdot 4 = 12$
   ÷2 ÷2
   $6 \cdot 2 = 12$

2. $4 \cdot 4 = 16$
   ÷2 ÷2
   $2 \cdot 8 = 16$

3. $2 \cdot 9 = 18$
   ÷3 ÷3
   $6 \cdot 3 = 18$

4. $6 \cdot 8 = 48$
   ·2 ÷2
   $12 \cdot 4 = 48$

5. $4 \cdot 5 = 20$
   ·2 ÷2
   $2 \cdot 10 = 20$

6. $6 \cdot 5 = 30$
   ÷2 ·2
   $3 \cdot 10 = 30$

7. $4 \cdot 6 = 24$
   ·2 ÷2
   $8 \cdot 3 = 24$

8. $6 \cdot 6 = 36$
   ÷2 ·2
   $3 \cdot 12 = 36$

9. $5 \cdot 8 = 40$
   ·2 ÷2
   $10 \cdot 4 = 40$

10. $10 \cdot 6 = 60$
    ÷2 ·2
    $5 \cdot 12 = 60$

119

Multiply/Divide by the Same Amount

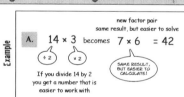

Example

A. 14×3 becomes $7 \times 6 = 42$
(÷2) (×2)
new factor pair
same result, but easier to solve

If you divide 14 by 2 you get a number that is easier to work with

SAME RESULT, BUT EASIER TO CALCULATE!

Rewrite these multiplication problems by multiplying & dividing by the same amounts

Your factor pairs should be normal times table numbers

1. 16×4
   ÷2 ×2
   $8 \cdot 8 = 64$
   new factor pair

2. 18×2
   ÷2 ×2
   $9 \cdot 4 = 36$
   new factor pair

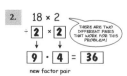

THERE ARE TWO DIFFERENT PAIRS THAT WORK FOR THIS PROBLEM!

3. 24×6
   ÷2 ×2
   $12 \cdot 12 = 144$
   new factor pair

SOMETIMES YOU HAVE TO TRY DIFFERENT COMBINATIONS UNTIL YOU GET A PAIR THAT IS EASY TO WORK WITH

4. 28×3
   ÷4 ×4
   $7 \cdot 12 = 84$
   new factor pair

5. 16×5
   ÷2 ×2
   $8 \cdot 10 = 80$
   new factor pair

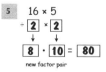

6. 32×3
   ÷4 ×4
   $8 \cdot 12 = 96$
   new factor pair

120

© Peter Wise 2016

Estimating with Decimals

ROUND the decimals first; then work the problem

Example

A. 5.8×4
↓
is about $\boxed{6} \times 4$ is about $\boxed{24}$

Round the decimals to the ONES place and then solve

1. 2.3×7
↓
is about $\boxed{2} \times 7$ answer is about $\boxed{14}$

2. 8.6×2
↓
is about $\boxed{9} \times 2$ answer is about $\boxed{18}$

3. 6.2×5
↓
is about $\boxed{6} \times 5$ answer is about $\boxed{30}$

4. 2.7×6
↓
is about $\boxed{3} \times 6$ answer is about $\boxed{18}$

5. 1.8×1.9
↓
is about $\boxed{2} \times \boxed{2}$ answer is about $\boxed{4}$

6. 3.14×9
↓
is about $\boxed{3} \times 9$ answer is about $\boxed{27}$

7. 5.3×2.8
↓
is about $\boxed{5} \times \boxed{3}$ answer is about $\boxed{15}$

8. $8.4 \div 2.3$
↓
is about $\boxed{8} \div \boxed{2}$ answer is about $\boxed{4}$

9. 3.6×7.4
↓
is about $\boxed{4} \times \boxed{7}$ answer is about $\boxed{28}$

10. $(4.8)^2$
↓
$\boxed{5}^2$ answer is about $\boxed{25}$

121

Distributive Property with Multiplication

Example

A. $4 \times 23 \quad (4 \times 20) + (4 \times 3)$

4 IS MULTIPLYING BOTH 20 AND 3!

$80 + 12 = \boxed{92}$

Do the calculations mentally

WHEN YOU BREAK APART A NUMBER THAT IS MULTIPLIED, THIS IS CALLED THE *DISTRIBUTIVE PROPERTY!*

Break up the two-digit numbers and multiply each digit separately

Calculate final answers mentally

1. 3×14
$(3 \times 10) + (3 \times 4) = \boxed{42}$
Do the calculations mentally

2. 2×46
$(2 \times 40) + (2 \times 6) = \boxed{92}$
Do the calculations mentally

3. 8×13
$(8 \times 10) + (8 \times \boxed{3}) = \boxed{104}$

4. 2×67
$(2 \times 60) + (2 \times \boxed{7}) = \boxed{134}$

5. 4×24
$(4 \times \boxed{20}) + (4 \times \boxed{4}) = \boxed{96}$
break up 24 into 20 + 4

6. 2×78
$(2 \times \boxed{70}) + (2 \times \boxed{8}) = \boxed{156}$
break up 78 into 70 + 8

7. 3×56
$(\boxed{3} \times \boxed{50}) + (\boxed{3} \times \boxed{6}) = \boxed{168}$

8. 4×27
$(\boxed{4} \times \boxed{20}) + (\boxed{4} \times \boxed{7}) = \boxed{108}$

9. 5×89
$(\boxed{5} \times \boxed{80}) + (\boxed{5} \times \boxed{9}) = \boxed{445}$

10. 7×36
$(\boxed{7} \times \boxed{30}) + (\boxed{7} \times \boxed{6}) = \boxed{252}$

122

Distributive Property with Multiplication

Break up the two-digit numbers and multiply each digit separately

1. 3×17
$(3 \times 10) + (3 \times 7) = \boxed{51}$
Do the calculations mentally

2. 2×97
$(2 \times 90) + (2 \times 7) = \boxed{194}$
Do the calculations mentally

3. 5×79
$(5 \times \boxed{70}) + (5 \times \boxed{9}) = \boxed{395}$

4. 8×23
$(8 \times \boxed{20}) + (8 \times \boxed{3}) = \boxed{184}$

5. 9×34
$(9 \times \boxed{30}) + (9 \times \boxed{4}) = \boxed{306}$

6. 4×36
$(4 \times \boxed{30}) + (4 \times \boxed{6}) = \boxed{144}$

7. 6×27
$(6 \times \boxed{20}) + (6 \times \boxed{7}) = \boxed{162}$
Do the calculations mentally

8. 4×84
$(\boxed{4} \times \boxed{80}) + (\boxed{4} \times \boxed{4}) = \boxed{336}$

9. 6×73
$(\boxed{6} \times \boxed{70}) + (\boxed{6} \times \boxed{3}) = \boxed{438}$

10. 7×28
$(\boxed{7} \times \boxed{20}) + (\boxed{7} \times \boxed{8}) = \boxed{196}$

11. 8×59
$(\boxed{8} \times \boxed{50}) + (\boxed{8} \times \boxed{9}) = \boxed{472}$

12. 9×65
$(\boxed{9} \times \boxed{60}) + (\boxed{9} \times \boxed{5}) = \boxed{585}$

123

Distributive Property with Multiplication

Break up the two-digit numbers and multiply each digit separately

1. 3×18
$(3 \times 10) + (3 \times 8) = \boxed{54}$
Do the calculations mentally

2. 4×13
$(\boxed{4} \times \boxed{10}) + (\boxed{4} \times \boxed{3}) = \boxed{52}$
Do the calculations mentally

3. 7×17
$(\boxed{7} \times \boxed{10}) + (\boxed{7} \times \boxed{7}) = \boxed{119}$

4. 6×29
$(\boxed{6} \times \boxed{20}) + (\boxed{6} \times \boxed{9}) = \boxed{174}$

5. 8×48
$(\boxed{8} \times \boxed{40}) + (\boxed{8} \times \boxed{8}) = \boxed{384}$

6. 9×32
$(\boxed{9} \times \boxed{30}) + (\boxed{9} \times \boxed{2}) = \boxed{288}$

7. 5×76
$(\boxed{5} \times \boxed{70}) + (\boxed{5} \times \boxed{6}) = \boxed{380}$

8. 6×34
$(\boxed{6} \times \boxed{30}) + (\boxed{6} \times \boxed{4}) = \boxed{204}$

9. 7×28
$(\boxed{7} \times \boxed{20}) + (\boxed{7} \times \boxed{8}) = \boxed{196}$

10. 4×64
$(\boxed{4} \times \boxed{60}) + (\boxed{4} \times \boxed{4}) = \boxed{256}$

11. 8×73
$(\boxed{8} \times \boxed{70}) + (\boxed{8} \times \boxed{3}) = \boxed{584}$

12. 3×908
$(\boxed{3} \times \boxed{900}) + (\boxed{3} \times \boxed{8}) = \boxed{2724}$
TREAT THE 9 & THE 0 AS A SINGLE NUMBER. WHAT NUMBER IS IT REALLY?

124

Distributive Property with Multiplication

Break up the two-digit numbers and multiply each digit separately

Do all calculations mentally

1. $4 \times 17 =$ **68**
2. $5 \times 15 =$ **75**
3. 6×17 **102**
4. $8 \times 13 =$ **104**
5. $3 \times 19 =$ **57**
6. $7 \times 16 =$ **112**
7. $9 \times 17 =$ **153**
8. $8 \times 14 =$ **112**
9. $7 \times 19 =$ **133**
10. $6 \times 13 =$ **78**

11. $2 \times 29 =$ **58**
12. $5 \times 27 =$ **135**
13. $6 \times 29 =$ **174**
14. $7 \times 38 =$ **266**
15. $9 \times 23 =$ **207**
16. $4 \times 29 =$ **116**
17. $7 \times 24 =$ **168**
18. $6 \times 26 =$ **156**
19. $3 \times 28 =$ **84**
20. $8 \times 24 =$ **192**

© Peter Wise 2016

125

Estimating with Multiplication

Example

round to the 10s place

A. $37 \rightarrow 40$
$\times 23 \rightarrow \times 20$ $= \boxed{800}$

ESTIMATE EACH NUMBER BEFORE MULTIPLYING

37 TIMES 23 IS ABOUT 800

Estimate by rounding both two-digit numbers and multiplying

ROUND THE 2-DIGIT NUMBERS TO THE NEAREST TEN!

1. $37 \rightarrow \boxed{40}$
$\times 23 \rightarrow \times \boxed{20}$ $= \boxed{800}$

2. $52 \rightarrow \boxed{50}$
$\times 68 \rightarrow \times \boxed{70}$ $= \boxed{3500}$

3. $67 \rightarrow \boxed{70}$
$\times 34 \rightarrow \times \boxed{30}$ $= \boxed{2100}$

DO THE NEXT TWO PROBLEMS MENTALLY!

4. 83
$\times 17$ $= \boxed{1600}$

5. 49
$\times 8$ $= \boxed{500}$

ROUND TO THE NEAREST 10!

ROUND THE 3-DIGIT NUMBERS TO THE NEAREST HUNDRED!

6. $287 \rightarrow \boxed{300}$
$\times 12 \rightarrow \times \boxed{10}$ $= \boxed{3000}$

7. $526 \rightarrow \boxed{500}$
$\times 28 \rightarrow \times \boxed{30}$ $= \boxed{15,000}$

8. $755 \rightarrow \boxed{800}$
$\times 38 \rightarrow \times \boxed{40}$ $= \boxed{32,000}$

DO #8-10 MENTALLY IF YOU CAN!

9. $439 \rightarrow \boxed{400}$
$\times 18 \rightarrow \times \boxed{20}$ $= \boxed{8000}$

10. $878 \rightarrow \boxed{900}$
$\times 24 \rightarrow \times \boxed{20}$ $= \boxed{18,000}$

© Peter Wise 2016

126

Estimating with Fractions

Example

THE FRACTION HAS TO EQUAL 1/2 OR MORE TO RAISE THE WHOLE NUMBER UP ONE!

A. $2\frac{1}{4} \times 3\frac{4}{5}$

$\boxed{2} \times \boxed{4}$

1/4 is less than 1/2, so we don't add 1 to the whole number

4/5 is closer to 1, so you add 1 to the 3

Estimate by rounding the fractions before calculating the amounts

1. $4\frac{5}{6} \times 3\frac{1}{6}$
$\boxed{5} \times \boxed{3}$ answer is about **15**

2. $5\frac{3}{4} \times 4\frac{9}{10}$
$\boxed{6} \times \boxed{5}$ answer is about **30**

3. $7\frac{1}{3} \times 5\frac{6}{7}$
$\boxed{7} \times \boxed{6}$ answer is about **42**

4. $11\frac{7}{9} \times 2\frac{4}{5}$
$\boxed{12} \times \boxed{3}$ answer is about **36**

5. $15\frac{2}{7} \times 1\frac{7}{8}$
$\boxed{15} \times \boxed{2}$ answer is about **30**

6. $19\frac{11}{12} \div 4\frac{1}{4}$
$\boxed{20} \div \boxed{4}$ answer is about **5**

7. $25\frac{5}{7} + 3\frac{3}{10}$
$\boxed{26} + \boxed{3}$ answer is about **29**

8. $14\frac{1}{3} - 2\frac{4}{5}$
$\boxed{14} - \boxed{3}$ answer is about **11**

9. $34\frac{5}{7} \div 6\frac{2}{3}$
$\boxed{35} \div \boxed{7}$ answer is about **5**

10. $20\frac{2}{5} \div 4\frac{7}{8}$
$\boxed{20} \div \boxed{5}$ answer is about **4**

© Peter Wise 2016

127

Four Times Table as Double-Double

Example

A. $4 \times \textcircled{3} =$ $3 \rightarrow \boxed{6} \rightarrow \boxed{12}$

double   double

START WITH THE NUMBER 4 IS MULTIPLYING!

A NUMBER DOUBLED TWICE IS THE SAME AS TIMES 4!

Solve the 4 times table calculations by doing the DOUBLE-DOUBLE trick

1. $4 \times \textcircled{2} =$ $2 \rightarrow \boxed{4} \rightarrow \boxed{8}$

2. $4 \times \textcircled{5} =$ $5 \rightarrow \boxed{10} \rightarrow \boxed{20}$

3. $4 \times \textcircled{10} =$ $10 \rightarrow \boxed{20} \rightarrow \boxed{40}$

4. $4 \times \textcircled{6} =$ $6 \rightarrow \boxed{12} \rightarrow \boxed{24}$

5. $4 \times \textcircled{8} =$ $8 \rightarrow \boxed{16} \rightarrow \boxed{32}$

6. $4 \times \textcircled{4} =$ $4 \rightarrow \boxed{8} \rightarrow \boxed{16}$

7. $4 \times \textcircled{9} =$ $9 \rightarrow \boxed{18} \rightarrow \boxed{36}$

8. $4 \times \textcircled{7} =$ $7 \rightarrow \boxed{14} \rightarrow \boxed{28}$

9. $4 \times \textcircled{12} =$ $12 \rightarrow \boxed{24} \rightarrow \boxed{48}$

© Peter Wise 2016

128

6 Times Table as Triple, Double

Example

A. $6 \times \textcircled{10} =$ $10 \xrightarrow{\text{times 3}} \boxed{30} \xrightarrow{\text{times 2 (or double)}} \boxed{60}$

START WITH THE NUMBER 6 IS MULTIPLYING!

ANY NUMBER TIMES 3, TIMES 2 IS THE SAME AS TIMES 6!

Solve the 6 times table calculations by doing the TRIPLE-DOUBLE trick

1. $6 \times \textcircled{2} =$ $2 \xrightarrow{\times 3} \boxed{6} \xrightarrow{\text{double}} \boxed{12}$

2. $6 \times \textcircled{5} =$ $5 \xrightarrow{\times 3} \boxed{15} \xrightarrow{\text{double}} \boxed{30}$

3. $6 \times \textcircled{3} =$ $3 \xrightarrow{\times 3} \boxed{9} \xrightarrow{\text{double}} \boxed{18}$

4. $6 \times \textcircled{8} =$ $8 \xrightarrow{\times 3} \boxed{24} \xrightarrow{\text{double}} \boxed{48}$

5. $6 \times \textcircled{6} =$ $6 \xrightarrow{\times 3} \boxed{18} \xrightarrow{\text{double}} \boxed{36}$

6. $6 \times \textcircled{9} =$ $9 \xrightarrow{\times 3} \boxed{27} \xrightarrow{\text{double}} \boxed{54}$

7. $6 \times \textcircled{7} =$ $7 \xrightarrow{\times 3} \boxed{21} \xrightarrow{\text{double}} \boxed{42}$

8. $6 \times \textcircled{4} =$ $4 \xrightarrow{\times 3} \boxed{12} \xrightarrow{\text{double}} \boxed{24}$

9. $6 \times \textcircled{12} =$ $12 \xrightarrow{\times 3} \boxed{36} \xrightarrow{\text{double}} \boxed{72}$

129

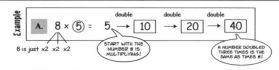

8 Times Table as Double-Double-Double

Example

A. $8 \times \textcircled{5} =$ $5 \xrightarrow{\text{double}} \boxed{10} \xrightarrow{\text{double}} \boxed{20} \xrightarrow{\text{double}} \boxed{40}$

8 is just ×2 ×2 ×2

START WITH THE NUMBER 8 IS MULTIPLYING!

A NUMBER DOUBLED THREE TIMES IS THE SAME AS TIMES 8!

Solve the 8 times table calculations by doing the DOUBLE-DOUBLE-DOUBLE trick

1. $8 \times \textcircled{3} =$ $3 \xrightarrow{\text{double}} \boxed{6} \xrightarrow{\text{double}} \boxed{12} \xrightarrow{\text{double}} \boxed{24}$

2. $8 \times \textcircled{7} =$ $7 \xrightarrow{\text{double}} \boxed{14} \xrightarrow{\text{double}} \boxed{28} \xrightarrow{\text{double}} \boxed{56}$

3. $8 \times \textcircled{10} =$ $10 \xrightarrow{\text{double}} \boxed{20} \xrightarrow{\text{double}} \boxed{40} \xrightarrow{\text{double}} \boxed{80}$

4. $8 \times \textcircled{2} =$ $2 \xrightarrow{\text{double}} \boxed{4} \xrightarrow{\text{double}} \boxed{8} \xrightarrow{\text{double}} \boxed{16}$

5. $8 \times \textcircled{4} =$ $4 \xrightarrow{\text{double}} \boxed{8} \xrightarrow{\text{double}} \boxed{16} \xrightarrow{\text{double}} \boxed{32}$

6. $8 \times \textcircled{6} =$ $6 \xrightarrow{\text{double}} \boxed{12} \xrightarrow{\text{double}} \boxed{24} \xrightarrow{\text{double}} \boxed{48}$

7. $8 \times \textcircled{8} =$ $8 \xrightarrow{\text{double}} \boxed{16} \xrightarrow{\text{double}} \boxed{32} \xrightarrow{\text{double}} \boxed{64}$

8. $8 \times \textcircled{9} =$ $9 \xrightarrow{\text{double}} \boxed{18} \xrightarrow{\text{double}} \boxed{36} \xrightarrow{\text{double}} \boxed{72}$

9. $8 \times \textcircled{12} =$ $12 \xrightarrow{\text{double}} \boxed{24} \xrightarrow{\text{double}} \boxed{48} \xrightarrow{\text{double}} \boxed{96}$

130

12 Times Table as Triple-Double-Double

Example

A. $12 \times \textcircled{2} =$ $2 \xrightarrow{\text{times 3 (or triple)}} \boxed{6} \xrightarrow{\text{double}} \boxed{12} \xrightarrow{\text{double}} \boxed{24}$

12 is just ×3 ×2 ×2

START WITH THE NUMBER MULTIPLYING 12!

Solve the 12 times table calculations by doing the TRIPLE-DOUBLE-DOUBLE trick

1. $12 \times \textcircled{3} =$ $3 \xrightarrow{\text{times 3 (= triple)}} \boxed{9} \xrightarrow{\text{double}} \boxed{18} \xrightarrow{\text{double}} \boxed{36}$

2. $12 \times \textcircled{4} =$ $4 \xrightarrow{\text{triple}} \boxed{12} \xrightarrow{\text{double}} \boxed{24} \xrightarrow{\text{double}} \boxed{48}$

3. $12 \times \textcircled{2} =$ $2 \xrightarrow{\text{triple}} \boxed{6} \xrightarrow{\text{double}} \boxed{12} \xrightarrow{\text{double}} \boxed{24}$

4. $12 \times \textcircled{7} =$ $7 \xrightarrow{\text{triple}} \boxed{21} \xrightarrow{\text{double}} \boxed{42} \xrightarrow{\text{double}} \boxed{84}$

5. $12 \times \textcircled{10} =$ $10 \xrightarrow{\text{triple}} \boxed{30} \xrightarrow{\text{double}} \boxed{60} \xrightarrow{\text{double}} \boxed{120}$

6. $12 \times \textcircled{6} =$ $6 \xrightarrow{\text{triple}} \boxed{18} \xrightarrow{\text{double}} \boxed{36} \xrightarrow{\text{double}} \boxed{72}$

7. $12 \times \textcircled{9} =$ $9 \xrightarrow{\text{triple}} \boxed{27} \xrightarrow{\text{double}} \boxed{54} \xrightarrow{\text{double}} \boxed{108}$

8. $12 \times \textcircled{8} =$ $8 \xrightarrow{\text{triple}} \boxed{24} \xrightarrow{\text{double}} \boxed{48} \xrightarrow{\text{double}} \boxed{96}$

9. $12 \times \textcircled{12} =$ $12 \xrightarrow{\text{triple}} \boxed{36} \xrightarrow{\text{double}} \boxed{72} \xrightarrow{\text{double}} \boxed{144}$

132

131

Mixed Review

Round the following numbers to the tenths place

1. 7.54 → $\boxed{7.5}$
2. 12.73 → $\boxed{12.7}$
3. 56.845 → $\boxed{56.8}$

Perform all four operations with the given numbers

		sum	product	difference	quotient
4.	30 5	$\boxed{35}$	$\boxed{150}$	$\boxed{25}$	$\boxed{6}$
5.	20 4	$\boxed{24}$	$\boxed{80}$	$\boxed{16}$	$\boxed{5}$
6.	12 3	$\boxed{15}$	$\boxed{36}$	$\boxed{9}$	$\boxed{4}$
7.	14 2	$\boxed{16}$	$\boxed{28}$	$\boxed{12}$	$\boxed{7}$

Break up the two-digit numbers and multiply each digit separately

8. 6×14

$(6 \times \boxed{10}) + (6 \times \boxed{4}) = \boxed{84}$

9. 8×37

$(8 \times \boxed{30}) + (8 \times \boxed{7}) = \boxed{296}$

Estimate by rounding the fractions before calculating the amounts

10. $5\frac{2}{3} \times 2\frac{1}{6}$
$\boxed{6} \times \boxed{2}$ answer is about $\boxed{12}$

11. $14\frac{11}{12} \div 4\frac{3}{4}$
$\boxed{15} \div \boxed{5}$ answer is about $\boxed{3}$

132

39258721R00099

Made in the USA
San Bernardino, CA
22 September 2016